TWO DAYS
= AND =
ONE
SUITCASE

❑ ❑ ❑

The True Story of One Family's Choice of
Friendship and Goodwill During World War II

By *Anne E. Neuberger*

And *Helen Hannan F*

In loving memory of
my dear parents L.J. and Nelle Hannan
and my dear sister Mari Hannan Brennan
and for my great brother Larry Hannan.
Special thanks to my son Tom Parra and niece Mary Johnson
for their tremendous help.
HHP

This story of family integrity is dedicated to my family.

Special thanks to Margaret Gaughan and Gregory Darr,
who believed this story should be told.
AEN

CONTENTS

Foreword

Things You Need To Know Before The Story Starts

My name is Helen. This story took place mostly in 1945, when I was 12 years old.

This is a true story and a really important one. Something took place in the United States back then that should never have happened.

I want to tell you this story because the more people, especially kids, know about it, the better the chance that this will never happen again.

I lived through it. I don't want this to be in our future.

It is up to you.

You will need a little background leading up to 1945, so here goes:

The whole world was at war. I mean the whole world! There were two groups of countries fighting each other. The ones called the Axis Powers were Germany, Italy and Japan. The other side, called the Allies, included Britain, France, Australia, Canada, New Zealand, India, the Soviet Union, China and the United States.

I counted and found that over 45 countries in all were affected by this war.

In other words, things were pretty bad all over.

Of course, there were millions and millions and millions of soldiers who fought in different ways. The lucky ones would come home, but many did not–at least 50 million.

And then there were all the medical people: medics and ambulance drivers, and hospitals workers of all kinds.

Food was a big deal, of course. Farmers and gardeners, people who packaged food, drivers who delivered food, storekeepers who sold it were all involved. Places where the war was being fought could not grow any food, so everywhere people were eating less, so what food there was could be shared.

This sharing was called rationing. That meant that people could only get certain amounts of food each month, or only certain groups of people got certain foods.

For example, we heard that in England kids under the age of 6 were the only ones who could have oranges because it was so hard to get oranges to that country. That would have left me out if I had been there.

Factories were changed. Places that made shoes, toys and new cars were now making war equipment. In homes and schools, people saved metal and rubber. Metal fences around schools or fancy homes were taken down. All these things were collected and taken to factories and made into bullets, bombs and tanks.

Changing what was produced meant that worn-out shoes and holey sweaters had to be mended, for no new ones were available. Nobody got new cars. It was hard to get enough gas to drive your car anyway.

There were fewer gifts and celebrations and big dinners during those years. We all coped.

Of course, this was nothing compared to what some people had to endure:

Those living in the areas of fighting were hiding, or just trying to survive in their homes if their homes were still standing. Whole sections of cities in some parts of the world were just piles of rubble. Many children were orphaned.

And we were just beginning to hear that some people had been forced into places often called "death camps."

Though people in the United States were worried, we did feel a little safer than people whose countries were directly in the war. At least the people I knew felt safer.

Later I would meet many Americans who were not safe at all.

PART
1

❏ ❏ ❏

PAPER DOLLS
and PEARL HARBOR

❏ ❏ ❏

USS Shaw Exploding in Pearl Harbor, 1941

My paper dolls were all lined up under the dining room table again. I propped them up against the trestle bar that secured the table legs and made myself comfortable with them. I was putting the yellow dress on one doll and was lost in my imagination.

This was my favorite spot. No one bothered me there, or needed me to pick up my stuff. It felt private even though I was actually near all the hubbub of my family. I was eight years old then, and we were living in Battle Creek, Michigan.

This wasn't actually home for me. Sometimes my dad, who was in the army reserve, would be sent to an army base, and the rest of us would go with him.

I will tell you about December 7th, 1941. It was snowy outside, very beautiful and peaceful. As she fixed a hole in my brother's sock, my mom hummed a Christmas carol. I think it was "Silent Night."

And then the front door burst open! A neighbor ran in and he was yelling!

"The Japanese have bombed Pearl Harbor! We're at war!"

The neighbor's unexpected and terrifying shout caused a flood of some horrible feeling to sweep through me. It felt like violent, rushing water. I didn't know what Pearl Harbor was, but I certainly knew the word "bombed."

My heart was beating very fast. I peeked out from under the table.

The neighbor man had already gone!

My mother was on her feet now. The sock and thread lay on the floor.

Dad leaped up from his chair, grabbed his coat, and left the house. I knew he would go immediately to the army base where he worked.

We didn't see him again for three days.

During that time, everyone else in my house and neighborhood was tense and quiet.

I quickly came to understand that everyone in the United States was also stunned.

Other parts of the world had been warring for three years. The United States had been watching, but not taking part. And then, the country of Japan attacked Hawaii, which was a territory of the United States. That changed everything for Americans.

My mom kept listening to the radio. My older sister and brother were always at the table, newspapers spread out, reading aloud to each other.

These newspapers had the biggest headlines I had ever seen. The letters were at least five inches high, printed in dark, demanding, scary letters that you couldn't ignore:

JAPAN OPENS WAR ON U.S.
1500 DEAD IN HAWAII
BOMBED!
IT'S WAR!!!
CONGRESS VOTES WAR

And there were photographs in the newspapers.

"Look at this," my brother, Larry, said. He moved over so I could see what he was reading.

From the territory called Hawaii, there were pictures of thick, billowing smoke rising from the bombed ships and downed airplanes in water near the shore.

Mari, my sister, was looking at another newspaper. "Here's President Roosevelt. And also pictures of the White House."

I saw our serious president, standing at a podium, surrounded by microphones, after he had signed the declaration of war. Other photos showed crowds of people huddled near the White House, hoping to be the first to get more information.

"What are those men doing?" I asked Larry as he continued to page through the paper.

We were looking at a picture of a large group of men. They were dressed in work clothes and lined up near some buildings in what appeared to be a big city.

"Their work is making equipment for the Navy. They live in New York City, but they have all volunteered to go to Hawaii to do their work there," Larry explained.

I saw articles about the need for blackout curtains. These were curtains made of heavy, dark fabric. When they were shut carefully at night, no light from a house or store could be seen. The idea was that any enemy planes flying overhead at night wouldn't bomb targets they couldn't see.

"Some cities are having air raid drills—lights off everywhere, and people in bomb shelters," Mari read. "Dayton, Ohio already has five shelters."

"Wow—listen to this," Larry said. "The lieutenant general, John L. DeWitt declared, 'This is war. Death and destruction may come from the skies at any moment.'"

I felt a little sick to my stomach, hearing that.

"Oh, no, listen to this!" Mari exclaimed. "A reporter asked President Roosevelt if the U.S. was open to enemy attack. He said, 'Enemy ships could swoop in and shell New York; enemy planes could drop bombs on war plants in Detroit; enemy troops could attack Alaska.'"

Then I saw something that caught my attention. I was a pretty good reader when I was 8 and so I chose to read this aloud, "The Army suggested that the White House be painted black in order for it to be harder for enemy bombers to target."

I sat there for a moment, trying to imagine the lovely White House painted black.

I wondered when my dad would come home. I decided to stick close to my mother.

Mom, Mari, Larry and I were all huddled near the radio when my dad finally came home.

He was wearing side arms. I had never seen a gun before.

I stared at that gun and looked at my dad. Despite all the pictures I had seen, it was my dad with a gun that told me something really serious had happened.

That is how the war began for me.

PART

2

❏ ❏ ❏

WHERE THE WAR TOOK US

❏ ❏ ❏

*United States military policemen reading about the German surrender
in the newspaper Stars and Stripes*

O n May 8, 1945, the church bells began ringing. Some were tolling in deep, rich tones as if they were serious; others sounded joyful. The city of St. Augustine in Florida was rejoicing!

The end of the war was finally in sight! Nazi Germany had surrendered!

And under all that thunderous sound were voices. People were singing, shouting, talking and laughing!

My dad was currently stationed in Florida, so my family was living there for a few months. But the people there were not the only ones who were joyful.

All across the United States people were also celebrating. In New Orleans there was dancing in the streets. And in New York City's Times Square, people rejoiced, standing shoulder to shoulder, waving flags, and holding up newspapers with huge headlines exclaiming, "It's Victory!" and "Nazis Quit!"

And it was not just in the United States where people celebrated. Great relief and joy spread across Europe too. After all, they had been fighting for six years! And much of the fighting was in their cities and lands.

This great day would be called VE Day, for Victory in Europe.

We listened to our president, Harry S. Truman, on the radio. He had become president only a few weeks ago, after the death of President Roosevelt.

Truman called for a day of thanksgiving. And he cautioned us that the war was only half over. We were still at war with Japan.

Of course, we were thankful. And we knew there was still more fighting to come. But for that day, we celebrated that a huge part of the war was finally, finally over!

Like many North Americans, my family was pretty safe and fairly comfortable. If we had stayed that way, our war story wouldn't be much to read. But, it didn't' stay that way.

In 1945, I was 12, Larry was 14 and Mari was almost 16. My parents' attitudes about what is right and what is wrong were based on what they thought Jesus asks of us. They did their best to pass these ideas on to us.

I could see that in Mari already. She was amazing. Sort of a Joan of Arc, who was brave and strong and did what was right, big time! And Mari was always thinking important things.

Larry was quieter. He was busy with school and sports. But he had important things on his mind too. Even though he was just a freshman in high school, he knew he wanted to go to law school. And he was always telling me why. He'd say, "The right lawyer can do a lot of good in the world." Our father was a great example of that.

My dad actually had two jobs. I mentioned that he was a major in the United States army. He was a Reserve Officer, and because of the war, he had been called up to active duty. But he was also a lawyer in civilian life.

In the army, he had different kinds of jobs, and sometimes being a lawyer became part of his army duties.

That's important, because that is what makes everything in this story happen.

Now that the war was ending, people were beginning to think about how they would go on with their lives.

I already mentioned that our family had gone with my dad when he was assigned to work in different army camps—that is why we were in Michigan when Pearl Harbor was bombed. We had moved six times in less than four years. It had been sort of fun!

Dad's last assignment in the army was at Camp Blanding in Florida. And it was his very last assignment because there he served under a general who was very prejudiced against Jewish people.

There was a young Jewish soldier who came from a successful and well-to-do family.

Perhaps the general resented his family's success? I wonder where these prejudices come from. In any case, he seemed to want to disgrace Private Goldfarb.

The young soldier was accused of a serious crime. He needed a lawyer.

Dad wasn't the only military lawyer. However, none of the others wanted to get involved with this case. They didn't want to bring the wrath of this general down on their heads!

But my dad, being the man he was, felt called to represent the young man. He knew what God asks of us when it comes to justice.

"I think the general is setting up Private Goldfarb. I am absolutely certain that young soldier is innocent," Dad told my mom.

He wasn't trying to convince her. Mom felt as strongly about these things as he did.

Dad wasn't being heroic. He knew what it would mean to his own military career if he took this case. And it wouldn't be good.

When he decided to defend the young man, Mom said, "Of course."

In the court martial, Dad got Private Goldfarb declared innocent.

We all cheered when Dad told us. We were proud of our father and we were happy and relieved for this soldier. He stayed in touch with our family, forever grateful to Dad.

But just as Dad expected, the general was furious. He got his revenge by ending my father's military career. That irate general saw to it that there was no going back for Dad.

This was sad because Dad really loved the army. He would have stayed on as a Reserve Officer. So far, he had served whenever he was needed. But clearly, the general had decided he was no longer needed.

During the war, Dad's normal army work was training new troops to go to Europe. And, thank God, this horrible war was almost over! New soldiers were no longer needed. Therefore neither was Dad. This was very convenient for that angry general who wanted to get my father out of the army altogether.

So Dad was deciding what was next for him in terms of work. I knew he was asking himself, "Where can I do the most good?"

We could just go back home. Chicago Title and Trust was holding his job for Dad. We owned a little bungalow in Park Ridge, Illinois, which my cousin was renting for now. I figured Mom would have loved to go back home to her garden and her tiny fruit tree orchard.

Just when we were all assuming we would be going back home, Dad heard something none of us had known about before.

"Nelle," he said to my mom as he came in the door. "I heard today that the government is looking for lawyers to work with something called the WRA."

Mom looked up from the bread dough she was kneading. "And that is?" she asked.

"Apparently it is a government agency."

"I have never heard of it," she said mildly.

"Neither have I," Mari said.

Dad said, "Nor has anyone else in our country, it seems. I think that is exactly the way the government wants it. WRA stands for War Relocation Authority.

"This agency manages numerous 'concentration' or 'relocation' centers, where our government imprisoned its own citizens of Japanese descent during the war."

Stunned silence.

And then Mari said, "Dad, what are you talking about?"

"Remember when Japan bombed Pearl Harbor in Hawaii? Many Americans, especially the people on the West Coast, became terrified that Japan might bomb our country just like they did Hawaii, or maybe even invade us."

I guess one or two of us nodded, for Dad went on.

"There has always been a lot of racial prejudice against the Japanese and Chinese who lived in our country. It has never been easy for them here. But with that bombing came a lot of fear that the Japanese living here might turn against us and try to help our enemy."

"Oh, this does not sound good," Mom said warily, wiping her hands on her apron.

"Rumors began flying around that caused white people to start mistrusting and mistreating their own neighbors who happened to be of Japanese descent."

"That's crazy," I said.

"Yes. But how our government reacted is even worse."

"How so?" Mom asked, but she looked like she was afraid to hear.

"A lot of high-ranking military and civilian officials began putting pressure on President Roosevelt to imprison our own citizens—in this case, Japanese-Americans."

"What did they do to be put into prison?" I asked.

"Nothing. None of them was ever even accused of a crime. There were no trials. No one was convicted of anything," Dad said.

"How many people are we talking about here?" Mari asked.

"Thousands. Many thousands."

I was stunned.

"You mean there are thousands of people in prisons somewhere, who haven't done anything wrong?" Mari asked.

Larry protested, "But our constitution says everyone is guaranteed a trial! It's called the 'due process of law'!"

"Yes, Larry, but these people were denied their rights," Dad said.

"But surely," Mom said, "President Roosevelt would not have allowed that!"

"At first, he was against their plan. He knew this was wrong morally and legally, and besides that, it wasn't even necessary to do it."

"But?" Mari asked.

"But he finally caved in to the pressure and signed the order."

"No!" Mom said.

"I am afraid so," Dad answered. "He signed it on February 19th in 1942. It is called Executive Order 9066."

I don't think I had ever seen my mother look so shocked.

My parents had always greatly admired President Roosevelt. He had done a great deal of good for our country and seen it through some really hard times. But this news really upset both of them. They felt this had been a terrible decision.

They believed that Roosevelt knew it was wrong but didn't have the moral courage to stand up to the evil people around him. Many of those people were prejudiced against Asian people and saw this as a way to hurt them. They just pretended that this was for the protection of the country.

To further explain to us kids why their feelings had changed so, Dad said, "The higher the position you are in and the more people that can be hurt by what you do, the greater the obligation you have to do the right thing, even when you are facing something very difficult."

I thought of my dad's courage to defend Private Goldfarb. He had done the right thing.

It probably won't surprise you that instead of going back to Park Ridge, my family was soon on our way to Colorado, to one of the relocation camps. Dad would help people who were imprisoned there.

PART
❸

❑ ❑ ❑

CAMP AMACHE, COLORADO

*Granada War Relocation Center, Colorado,
more commonly called Camp Amache.*

U.S. National Archives and Records Administration

We were leaving Florida. Everyone worked together to pack up the big, old Packard convertible. With five people, we had a fair amount of stuff so Dad attached a trailer to the back of the car. This trailer was small, especially for our big car. And old. It was from 1924, so it was now about 20 years old. But that is not what worried Larry. It was the wooden wheels that concerned him.

He walked around the back of the car, looking at the heap of suitcases and boxes that filled the little trailer, and squatted down to examine the wheels. He shook his head and asked Mom, "Do you really think this will make it all the way to Colorado?"

From behind a bag of bedding she was carrying, Mom asked distractedly, "What did you say, Larry?" But before he could reply, she said, "Helen, would you run back and go through each room to make sure we haven't left anything? And Mari..."

Larry was also given a job. Those completed, we climbed into the old car and headed west.

The sun was just rising. As usual when we started a trip, Mom led us all in a prayer to our guardian angels to watch over us as we traveled.

Then Larry said, "That house in Florida just might be the craziest place we have ever lived."

Mari laughed. "I agree! More happened in that house in one year than in my whole life!"

"Well, yes–there was the hurricane," Mom said.

Watching the Florida landscape as we left it behind I remembered that hurricane. It had been in October. Our little house was on a tiny island, just off the coast. Dad was on the mainland, on an army base. He must have been so worried when the hurricane hit! He probably knew how quickly that storm could cover the entire island.

Of course, I had been terrified we would all drown. I didn't know that the Coast Guard would come. But they did, and we were soon safe in their station. Wet, without our stuff, and a little shaken up, but safe!

I was amazed when they told us, "You can sleep in our beds—we won't have time to sleep." They weren't kidding. Those brave Guardsmen rescued many others.

Then they cooked us all fried chicken! It was so good! It seemed like they knew how to take care of just about anything.

A baby arrived without a bottle, because in the hurry to get out of the storm, that had been lost. They managed to find one for him.

And one of the guardsmen pulled a man's tooth! When he arrived, the poor guy was all wet and shook up, but he also had a terrible toothache. He was intending to get it pulled, but then the hurricane arrived. His cheek was swollen, and he was really in pain. So they took care of that too!

"The Coast Guardsmen were like knights on white horses," I said. "They will always be heroes to me."

"You and me both," Mom said. "I was so relieved to get to that station!"

"How did you feel when we went back to the house after the storm had passed?" Mari asked, with a grin.

We all laughed, remembering when we arrived back and opened the door. Water came pouring out! And on this wave of water came a baby snake, Dad's tie to his dress uniform and Mom's copy of "The Army Wife."

"That book is supposed to help women learn how to cope with whatever happens in an army life," Mom said, chuckling. "But it never said a word about hurricanes!"

"A serious omission," Mari said.

"I think you all coped extremely well in that crisis," Dad said and added, "True bravery."

"Well, we waved goodbye to that baby snake and went ahead to try and clean up the mess the storm left," I said.

Dad looked at me via the rear view mirror and smiled.

"Speaking of bravery," Larry said, "we got used to those big snakes that kept showing up in our backyard."

"Whose backyard?" Mari said. "You never saw me go out there!"

I had to agree. None of us humans spent time in the yard. Because the house was on the edge of the jungle-like area on that part of the island, huge snakes used to slither out from the shadier jungle and sun themselves in our sunny yard. Or their yard.

"I wonder how those snakes coped with the fires," I said.

The plants in the jungle seemed to catch fire and burn easily. There was no fire department on the island. We had quickly learned that we could fight small fires. I remembered the day Mom and I smelled smoke and looked out the window to see a fire not too far from the house. Larry and Mari had already realized the situation. They were there, using branches from myrtle trees to beat down the flames. Mom and I ran out to help them and we soon had that fire out.

That happened a few times.

But then came the big fire. All those little fires and huge snakes and even the hurricane didn't prepare us for that night.

"I bet you weren't worried about how the snakes were coping when we had that serious fire!" Larry said. "Mari, you were the true hero that night."

I agreed. I could tell my mother was shuddering a little at this story. She and my dad were exchanging glances.

Mari was 15 and just learning to drive. A 1937 tow truck had been left in the yard of our rental house. Who knows why? But thank God it had been!

This old and large truck had something called compound gears and Mari was learning how to drive using that monster. The wife of one of Dad's sergeants was her teacher.

Dad was on the army base, so it was just Mom, Mari, Larry and me. It was late and we had gone to bed. I was sleeping already when we heard a loud banging on the door and a neighbor screaming, "Get out! Get out!!"

I will never forget the confusion and fear that flooded me as I jumped out of bed. The smell of fire was spilling into the house. Mom was yelling, "Larry, you and Helen get into the truck!"

We ran out the door, barefoot and in pajamas. There seemed to be flames coming from all directions!

I hadn't stopped running or even slowed down, but Larry shouted, "Come on Helen!"

We reached the back of the truck and scrambled onto it. I must have hit my knee because much later I realized it was scraped and bloodied.

Mom and Mari were close behind us and despite the smoke and fear I saw that Mari had the truck keys clasped in her fist.

Now Larry said, "Dad, you should have seen Mari that night! She managed to get that old truck started, shift all those gears and floor it!"

What always amazed me most about Mari was her ability to stay cool, no matter what. That night was the very best example! Rolling flames were on both sides of the road now and she, barely a driver yet, was able to get that truck going.

Mari said, "I think I was only able to get it up to about 10 miles an hour."

"The road was only about eight feet wide and really, we were between two walls of fire, and that truck could not go fast," Mom said. "But Mari kept her concentration and got us out of there. You saved us, Mari. You really did. Every time I think of that, I thank God that we all escaped unharmed!"

We exchanged a few other memories that were lighter and even funny, but the trauma of the fire was still with me, like the smell of the smoke that never really washed out of my pajamas.

By the next day, we had left behind both Florida and Alabama. The big Packard was humming along in Mississippi, with the little trailer bumpity-bumping along behind.

"I was thinking about all the misadventures you had with the house on the island," Dad said. "Remember when we first got there and we were told the story about the people that had lived there just before us?"

"The spy!" I said.

"Yeah, we missed all that fun," Larry said.

Before we came to the little island, a woman lived in the house. Her husband was a Navy flyer, so he was gone a lot. She was not healthy and needed to rest a lot. So the house must have been very quiet. The neighbors were not very close, either.

As the story goes, the woman was resting one afternoon and she distinctly heard someone walking right above her. Stealthily, cautiously, but distinctly— someone was walking across the upstairs floor! She screamed and jumped up. In the next room, she saw feet emerging from the attic trap door! The rest of a man followed, hitting the floor and running out the door. She ran to the window and saw him disappear into the jungle. Then she called Naval Intelligence—there was no police force on the island.

When they arrived, they found all kinds of equipment in the attic. Apparently the man was a German spy! Probably he had been put ashore by a German submarine. He was never found, so probably when he stopped making contact, they must have realized he was in trouble and picked him up at a prearranged place. At least that is what the Naval officials conjectured.

Once we moved in, we heard that story. Of course Dad and Larry climbed up into the attic, but there was no trace of the spy. Naval Intelligence had done its work thoroughly, leaving only some sleepy spiders.

Speaking of sleepy, I was getting tired as we kept on rolling along. It was dark now and we were in a swampy area of Louisiana.

The three of us kids were dosing when suddenly there was a sound I couldn't identify. Larry, Mari and I all sat upright. It had come from the back of the car, and now there was a feeling as if something was off balance. Dad slowed down as quickly as he could.

"It's the trailer," Mari predicted.

As soon as the car stopped, we got out.

The taillights of the car were not strong enough for us to see what had happened to the trailer. Mom found a flashlight in the car and held it as Dad and Larry squatted to examine it. A wheel had broken right off down to the axel.

I looked at that forlorn little trailer, piled with our things. It was as if the car had been too powerful for it and the trailer had decided now was as good as any to submit its resignation.

We couldn't just leave it there, and besides, there was no more room in the trunk of the car for the stuff in the trailer. But it was obvious the little trailer wasn't going anywhere without help. For a minute, we all looked around, as if hoping we might see some place to go for help, yet we all knew there wasn't any.

We were completely alone in pitch dark, not a gleam of light except our car lights. No streetlights, no warm homey glow from houses, not even the glare from oncoming cars. It had been hours since we had passed through any town, and no haze of lights up ahead promised one soon.

We really didn't know where we were. We knew we would eventually come to Baton Rouge, but we really weren't sure even where that was.

I began having the uneasy feeling we were in the jungle again.

"Do you think there are snakes here but we can't see them?" I asked.

"Naw," Larry said cheerfully. "Probably just crocodiles."

"I think crocodiles are only in Florida," Mari said. "But there could be alligators."

Mom said, "If you two think your jokes are making me feel better, you are wrong!"

Quickly Dad said, "In any case, let's go back to the car to figure out what we are going to do."

It did not take long before there was a plan. Since the only city we knew of was Baton Rouge, we would head in that direction. Our new driver, Mari, was going to drive there, unless we found a town with a tow truck before that. Mom, Larry and I were going to go with her. Dad would stay with the trailer as it contained most of our clothing, bedding, etc., until we returned with help.

He unhitched the broken trailer from the car. We had a kerosene lantern with us, which would serve as a signal for us when we returned as well as a little light for Dad until we did. I hoped it would scare off any animals.

He lit it and cheerfully waved us off. With Mari at the wheel, we left. I looked back and watched the light from the lantern get smaller and smaller.

In the car, we prayed. It was fairly late and a Saturday night, not ideal for finding someone to help. However, God seemed to send us to a person named Mr. Gonzales. He had a truck, a big trailer and a willing heart. He followed us as we made our way back to Dad.

It had taken us hours to get to a city and then find our helper. Now the road back seemed even longer and darker. It was a winding road but Mari carefully found our way back. I watched for the lantern light and was excited and relieved when I saw a tiny spark up ahead that grew bigger as we got closer.

Finally we saw Dad, huddled over the lantern. Not a single vehicle had passed him in all the long time he had been out here.

I bet he had been praying too!

Mr. Gonzales and Dad got to work right away. They pushed the broken trailer onto the big trailer hitched to Mr. Gonzales' truck.

It was decided that Dad would ride with Mr. Gonzales and the rest of us would follow in the car. The truck started off and

Mari again got behind the steering wheel of the car. She had to turn it around.

What we didn't know and couldn't see was that there was no shoulder at all on either side. How Mr. Gonzales turned around, we'll never know because we weren't concerned about that when he had been turning. But now Mari had to turn and she did not know this: if you strayed an inch you went over into a very deep ditch. Well, Mari did, and we did, and there we sat with our headlights pointing up into the trees!

For some brief seconds, we sat in stunned silence. Then Mom said, "Everyone alright?" We were all unhurt and now we began to evaluate the situation.

Dad and Mr. Gonzales were far enough ahead that they didn't realize what had happened to us. They assumed we were following them but out of sight because of the many turns in the road. We didn't know when they would realize this and come back.

But that was not really the problem right now!

Our car had become wedged between some trees. Who knows how far we would have slid down—and into what—had the trees not stopped us. So that was good. But the angle our car and the great weight of it kept us from opening the doors to escape. So there we sat.

We knew that few, if any, cars would pass by. Even if there were some traffic, drivers would most likely not even see us in this darkness.

We were miles from anywhere, so even if we could get out of the car, it was pointless to risk walking along an unknown road in the dark, with no lights, not even much of a moon, to guide us.

I have mentioned that our family has always been big on prayer, but I think this time we outdid ourselves.

And then help showed up. I will tell you what happened, and you see if you can figure out how this came about. I have mulled over this and the only answer I can reach is that this was a miracle. Angels maybe. Probably.

The silence and darkness of that scary night was suddenly broken by the arrival of an enormous logging truck.

How it even fitted on that narrow road, I will never know. From it climbed two men. They were the tallest people I had ever seen. They walked over to where we had gone off the road as if they already knew we were there. They stood there, studying the situation.

We watched, wildly hopeful now for the first time in a couple of hours. And a little puzzled that these men neither spoke to us or to each other.

They went back to their truck and returned with a huge log chain. This they were able to wrap around the front of our big car, which was pretty much sticking straight up.

Inside the car, we marveled at their quick work and skill and wondered what was next.

Those silent helpers got back into their truck and slowly, slowly, pulled us until our car was back on the road!

We were bumped and jostled, but what relief we felt!

Mom was now able to reach her purse and was looking for money to pay them. They got out of their truck and took the chain off of our car, and put it back onto their truck. They began to climb into their truck.

They still had not spoken to us or connected with any of us with a smile or a wave. But they had saved us!

Mom jumped out of our car and ran to them, a $10 bill in her hand. It was all she had with her. They accepted it, but still did not speak to her as she thanked them. The truck started up and off they went around the next curve.

Mari started our car, none the worse for its time in the trees. Mom joined us and we all began talking at once.

"The road is so narrow!" Larry exclaimed. "I don't know how such a huge truck could even use this road!

"Why was a logging truck out on this road so late on a Saturday night?" I wondered.

"I don't know how they could possibly turn enough to pull us out!" Mari said. "I barely began turning when we were going down into the ditch!"

"And why didn't they speak to each other or us?" Mom pondered.

Our wonder about our helpers intensified as we continued our journey. Where were they now?

Mari had started to drive almost immediately after our helpers had left, going around the same curve they had just driven. But there was no sign of that big truck.

All the way through the swamp, around tight curves on a very narrow road in pitch darkness, they would have had to drive that gigantic truck very slowly. And our car had a powerful engine. We should have easily caught up. But we never did.

"They must have turned off somewhere," Larry said.

But we had all been watching for turnoffs they might have taken. There weren't any.

"It just doesn't make any sense," Mari said.

"Angels?" I said.

"Well, there doesn't seem to be any other explanation," Mom said.

The rest of the trip was uneventful, especially compared to that night! We reconnected with Dad, found a new trailer and got back on the road.

A few days later, we were finally getting closer to Colorado. Everyone was getting tired of traveling and trying not to complain too much.

I think we were also all wondering about what our next temporary home would be like. All we really knew about it was that it was called Camp Amache and also known as the Granada War Relocation Center.

"Well, we will see what it is like when we get there," said Mom. "In any case, it is a special day!"

"Mari's birthday!" I exclaimed.

Dad whistled. "Sixteen!" he said, sounding like he couldn't quite believe it.

Larry started a round of "Happy birthday!"

Mari grinned at each of us.

Several hours later, cruising down Highway 385, Dad said we were getting close.

It was very flat. I felt as if I could see miles in all directions.

"I thought there would be mountains!" I said. Obviously I hadn't asked enough questions.

Observing the land from his side of the car, Larry said, "Amache is tucked into the bottom corner of Colorado. We're close to Kansas and Oklahoma. We aren't near the mountains."

I knew from geography class that meant we were on the prairie now. With the car windows open, the wind whipped through our hair.

"Is that a fence up ahead?" Dad asked.

We all peered out the windshield, saying nothing, trying to see just what this was.

"Yes," Mari said finally. "A wire fence. And it is topped with barbed wire!"

As we drove along it, I noticed the four strands of wire running between posts were also barbed. Then the wire on top looked like a tangle of more barbed wire. It made me think of a fierce animal with bared teeth. That fence seemed to run on forever.

The area looked desert-like to my Midwestern eyes. It was very dry, and there were not many trees. I saw scrubby grass and something that looked like some kind of cactus. And yet, enclosed by the fence were rows and rows of cultivated land, where a multitude of crops were flourishing. I recognized corn and wheat.

Dad was noticing this too. "I think those are sugar beets over there."

"Potatoes and onions," Mom added.

"Do you think the people held in Amache are doing this farming?" Mari asked.

"It's very possible," said Dad.

If those lovely fields had not been surrounded by that hateful fence, I would have felt better.

Judging by the silence as we drove on, I think we all felt as flat as the land we were traveling on.

A few minutes later, Mom said, "Is that the entrance over there?"

Near it was a tower with windows. "Is that a guard tower?" Mari asked.

"I suppose so," Dad said, turning the car into the entrance.

We waited at the closed gate as a guard approached our car.

I was terrified and grabbed Mari's hand. The guard was wearing big and very dusty boots and his pants legs were tucked into them. Around his waist was a belt with many pockets on it, and a small flashlight was dangling from it. On his head was a helmet that looked a lot like an upside down soup bowl. But I was so scared I couldn't laugh, for in his hands was a very long gun with what looked like a knife sticking out of the shooting end.

Needless to say, there was no cheery hello.

"State your business here," he said.

Dad showed his ID and explained he was a lawyer sent by the WRA.

The guard peered into the back seat. I could hardly breath. Mari gave my hand a little comforting squeeze.

"You will need to go to the main office," he said, and gave directions. He opened the gate and Dad drove through.

I was 12 years old and I was in prison.

Dad went into the office. The rest of us stayed in the car. We were quiet, but Mom turned around and gave us a reassuring smile. I felt a rush of love towards her. My gentle, brave mother!

Dad was soon coming out the door with a key in hand. He jumped into the car and said we were assigned an apartment where the military police were housed.

I think I gave a little squeak of fear, so Dad explained, "I think it will be fine. They are putting us there just because we wouldn't fit into the staff quarters."

Dad pointed out those quarters. They were a collection of little white cottages, all clustered around an area of green grass, like a village square. Around all of this was a cheerful white picket fence.

When Dad said we wouldn't fit into the staff quarters, he meant there were no available cottages there now. But we were to find out that there were many ways in which we would not have fit in there!

We didn't have far to go to get to our quarters. As Dad drove, I looked around from the backseat window. There were more guard towers. I'd count them sometime. By now I felt less frightened and more curious about other aspects of this place.

In contrast to the cheerful little village green and its white fence, the rest of the camp seemed colorless. There were no trees nearby but there was sand and dirt—everywhere.

"I imagine this sand can really get into your eyes on a very windy day," Mari said.

Dad nodded. "I suppose whatever was growing here was cleared to build these barracks, and what was underneath was this very sandy soil. With nothing growing on it, it just blows all over."

"I wonder whose land it is—or at least who owned it before this was built here," Mom said quietly.

"Me too," Dad said.

"I think there are searchlights on those guard towers," Larry said, looking up.

"We'll find out tonight," Mari said. "But aren't you surprised that this so-called camp is like a town? I didn't know it would have things like a post office!"

I nodded. Besides the administration buildings and staff housing there was a hospital, a little store, a small library and barracks used as churches. Later we would find out that there were police and fire departments as well as a newspaper office.

Dad stopped the car outside the housing where we were to stay. Getting out of the car after hours of riding, I stretched and looked around. Dad was facing away from us.

Gesturing, he said, "And there is the fine housing for the people who are forced to live here."

Not too far away, but definitely segregated from our housing, were rows and rows and more rows of barracks like you would see on an army base. We would learn that there were 29 "blocks" of barracks. In each block there were 12 buildings, or barracks, and in each of these were at least five "apartments."

We were in a land that seemed to go on forever, but the people were living in tiny spaces.

Mari was looking towards the building we would be living in. It too was a barracks, but much bigger.

"Why can't we live with the people who are imprisoned here?" Mari asked. She sounded skeptical. That was a word I had learned recently.

"I imagine they are giving us a bigger place," Mom said. She was using her calm voice, but I knew she was feeling the injustice Mari was about to point out.

I guess I knew my mother and sister pretty well, for the very next thing Mari said was, "That doesn't sound very fair!"

"None of this is fair," Dad said. "And that is why we are here, to help create a little bit of fairness if we can."

He picked up a suitcase and a box and headed to the door of our place. The rest of us scrambled to do the same.

Once inside, Mom was delighted. "Three bedrooms! And a good-sized room for gathering and eating!" she said. "And look at this kitchen—lots of cabinets and an electric stove! And a refrigerator!"

It was not nearly as nice as our home in Illinois, but as my mother believed so strongly in why we were here, she overlooked that.

And it was OK. We began unpacking and making this space our temporary home.

We made up the beds and unpacked the kitchen things.

"I'm hungry," Larry said and I agreed I was too.

Mom was looking around the kitchen supplies and said a little wistfully, "I wish I could make Mari a birthday cake." In a little louder voice she announced, "We will have to eat in the communal dining room until we can get to a grocery store."

Larry grinned. "Communal dining room, Mom? You mean the mess hall?"

Mom grinned right back at him. She was just trying to put a positive spin on it.

None of us knew what this dining room/mess hall would be like. But we were hungry and besides, eating there would be a good way to get into life here and meet people.

We headed off to the nearest one. I looked back at the white picket fence and the white cottages of the camp staff. I assumed that most of the staff were white people, or European-Americans. Did they choose to live very separately from the Japanese-Americans? If that were so, it seemed kind of weird to me because we were all inside this fence, with not much to do. It seemed to me that making friends would be the first thing you would do.

And, of course, that is what Mari did.

We reached the mess hall and joined a line of people. It was so long that we were standing outside the building for a few minutes. I wondered what it was like in the winter. Did people have to stand in line outside for every meal then too?

People looked at us with curiosity, but they smiled in a polite, friendly way.

Once inside, I saw that the mess hall could have been a map of the barracks: rows and rows of rectangular tables.

The place was packed. We were the only non-Japanese there. I guess I would have felt uncomfortable, but both of my parents were already chatting and laughing with others.

Soon they were introducing us. I sensed that the internees, as we would come to call the people forced to live here, were glad our family was eating in the hall.

Again I wondered about the staff people. Did they ever eat here? And what about the guards? Where did they eat?

We each got a tin plate that had three sections. There were no choices to make about food. I watched as a hot dog and bun were put on my plate, then a spoonful of potatoes, a spoonful of rice and some beets. I asked for milk.

The man serving me said, "And you are under 5 years old?" He had a little smile on his face so I figured he was teasing me.

"Of course not—I am 12!" I said, with a grin back at him.

"Then, no milk for you," he said cheerfully.

Apparently you have to be less than 5 years old to get milk! I would miss milk.

We sat down at one of the tables, which looked like the picnic tables you see in parks—heavy wooden structures with attached benches. I always bump my knees trying to get in or out of those. This time was no exception.

I sat next to Larry and rubbed my now bruised knee. "They won't give us any milk," I whispered to Larry. "You have to be under 5."

"Yeah. They seemed sort of shocked when I asked for it," Larry said. He was looking at his plate. I knew he was hungry, but he clearly wasn't excited about the food in front of him.

It was so crowded that my arm was up against Larry's arm. But at our table, at least, there was a cheerful atmosphere and Dad asked others questions. And he began telling them stories of his army experiences. My dad made friends everywhere.

Larry finished his food quickly. He looked over at the food line, but some people still were in line to get their food. It didn't look as if getting seconds was going to happen.

Mom was watching Larry too. We both knew he was still hungry. Silently, Mom put some of her potatoes on his plate. Larry gave her a grateful smile.

Two girls were heading over to our table. I recognized them as part of the serving crew. They were about Mari's age.

"Hello," said one of these girls. "I am Mollie Fugimoto and this is my sister, Edna. We want to wish Mari happy birthday!"

We were amazed. How could they have possibly known it was her birthday? We never did find out!

They were so friendly and welcoming, and of course, Mari was never shy. They began talking—and they have been talking ever since!

We left the mess hall, heading back to our barracks. We had arrived there not knowing anyone, but as we left, we were saying good-bye to numerous people!

That was a good feeling. It was strange, though, that everyone else was headed to a different part of the camp than we were.

Mom and Dad were talking quietly, but we kids could hear them.

"I had no idea anything like this existed," Mom said.

"Nor I," said Dad. "We have seen lots of Army camps but nothing on earth prepared me for this."

"It stunned me to see sweet little toddlers and gentle elderly women all locked up in a prison with soldiers with guns hovering over them. I feel as if I can't really take that all in! It seems so unbearably wrong!" Mom said heatedly.

I had been caught up in meeting kids at dinner, but listening to my parents, I realized I had had the same feeling in the pit of my stomach all through the mess hall experience.

Larry was looking up at the guard tower. I knew he was waiting to see if they actually used the searchlights.

From a distance, from one of the barracks where the families lived, I heard a baby cry. I slipped my hand into my dad's hand and walked with him the rest of the way back.

After all the driving and moving in, everyone was tired. I was glad we had made up our beds before we had gone to eat. Mari and I were sharing one of the bedrooms and were in bed soon after we got back.

Once in bed, however, my mind kicked in with lots of questions. I was silent at first, trying to imagine what it would be like to be forced to live here.

I sorted through what I did understand: our family was choosing to go here, but most of the people here had been forced to come, forced out of their homes, their schools and their jobs. They had no choice but to leave their whole lives behind them! And they had been here a few years already! But soon they would be allowed to leave the camps. For that, they would be needing help to get their lives back.

"Why?" I said aloud suddenly, determined to understand. "Why did these places happen? The whole world was at war, but why should one group of Americans be put into jail—it sure seems like jail to me."

"It is jail," Mari agreed. She was clearly more tired than I was, but being the big sister she was, she went on. "As Dad said, there has always been a lot of prejudice against Japanese immigrants and their families in the United States—years before all this happened. The majority live on the West Coast. Many farm the rich lands of California and a lot of the food we eat comes from their farms. They have lived there for a few generations. Like everyone else, they are mostly good people who work hard and love their kids, pray and play and have birthdays too!"

"But even though others have always been prejudiced against them, they weren't in jail then. What happened to put them into these centers?" I wondered.

"Remember? It started when the country of Japan bombed that place in Hawaii? Pearl Harbor? That day, Japan became our enemy. The Japanese-Americans look like this enemy. I don't imagine that many of them have any more connection to Japan than we do to Ireland."

Mari rolled over onto her side, ready to sleep. But I kept talking.

"So you are saying their only "crime" was to look like the enemy? I am incredulous." Another new word for me.

"So am I, Helen. All Americans should be. "

We were silent for a moment.

"I've never met anyone Japanese-American before tonight, have you?" I asked.

"No, but what difference does it make? They are people and they have been badly mistreated. They need help, so we should help them," she said.

My mind was wide-awake now and I couldn't resist talking more.

"I know that now that the war is almost over, the people in these centers will be able to leave pretty soon. I guess they have lots of legal problems like what happened to their homes and businesses and Dad will try to help with those. I think it's great that Mom and Dad are willing to move to one of these places to help...."

"But?" Mari said, knowing I was working up to a question.

"But no one else I know even seems to know about these places! We have never talked in school about the Japanese-Americans. I have never heard any other adults mention these so-called camps. Nobody ever talks about this except our family! Why?"

"It has been a really, really well-kept secret, I guess. I don't understand that part of it either, Helen. But I do know that Mom and Dad talk about doing what is right, doing what God asks of us. They don't just talk, they do it. That's why we are here. And that is pretty amazing."

There came a soft knock at the door. Mari and I looked at each other a little guiltily. Were Mom or Dad having trouble sleeping because we were still talking?

But it was Larry. "Heard you two were still awake. I just wanted you to know that if you look out the window on the front of the apartment, you will see that there is a searchlight roaming around," he said. Then he grinned and added, "Sleep well, knowing you are well guarded." He closed the door.

Mari and I chuckled, but she said, "Let's go to sleep." She rolled over onto her side.

"Good night, Mari, and happy birthday," I said.

In the morning I wandered out of the bedroom, yawning and stretching. It was Sunday. Our family always went to Sunday Mass together.

"It's amazing, but this place even has its own Catholic church," Dad said. "We won't have to drive into the town."

It was a pleasant, very warm July day as we walked over the dust and sand towards a barracks that served as a church. I was happy to see that we were among many other families on their way to Mass too.

The searchlights were, of course, turned off. Still, there were guards in them, looking down at us. I wondered if the other kids, walking with their parents, were trying not to look up at the guard tower. Maybe they were used to it. But could you ever get used to living in a place where someone you didn't know was always watching you? Someone with a gun?

Along with many other people, we entered the barracks-church. I looked around curiously.

Of course it was not beautiful as churches are, being makeshift and, well, a barracks! Still, there was an altar of sorts: a long table covered with a snowy-white cloth, with a crucifix on a stand, a Roman Missal for all the prayers and candle holders.

The candles were beeswax, and these were burning bravely on this sunny morning. I caught a faint whiff of that wonderful smell that only beeswax gives.

My family sat down on a bench. My mother bowed her head and closed her eyes. She was really good at praying. As usual when sitting in a church, my thoughts wandered all over the place.

There was a small, portable organ in the corner, but no one seemed to be getting ready to play it. Some people were gathering, though, in a way that made me guess they were the choir. They held what I guessed were songbooks.

In a corner was a small shrine of sorts. Someone had placed a tiny statue of Mary, Jesus' mother, on a little, makeshift table. It stood on a square of cloth that someone had embroidered.

Back home, there were large, beautiful statues of Mary in churches, often with fresh bouquets of colorful flowers nearby. Someone here must have tried to make something a little like that. I felt sad for the person who could only do this tiny thing.

I looked at the crucifix with the suffering Jesus. There was a lot of suffering in the world. Maybe that is why Jesus died—to be with us when we suffer.

I looked around at all the people. We were the only non-Japanese there. It occurred to me that though this was my family's first morning here, those sitting with us had been here for at least three years.

Were none of the other non-Japanese people in camp Catholic? If they were, they must have gone to church someplace else.

Then I wondered who the priest would be.

As if on cue with my thoughts, Father John Swift entered. Of course, Mass was about to start, so that is why he really came in.

He had on the vestments priests normally wear for Mass. The top part was green, because this time of year was called Ordinary Time, and the church color for that is always green.

The choir began to sing. I realized I was surprised at how "normal" this little church was, in so abnormal a place as this prison camp.

But then, when you sing and pray with others while candles flicker, a barracks can become a church.

Of course everything that was said or sung was in Latin, until it was time for Father Swift to talk with us about what the readings were about. That was when I realized that though he was not Asian, he spoke fluent Japanese.

As I went up to take Communion, I had a feeling of being part of this group. I was very new to this place, I was there for different reasons than the others were, and we had different cultures. But still, we were all the same family in church.

I knelt down after Communion and thought about this: communion, community. They were sort of the same word. I liked feeling a part of this community.

After Mass, we stood around, meeting many others. Mollie and Edna came to talk briefly with Mari before they left with their parents. Again, I felt that spirit of welcome I had experienced at the mess hall.

Father Swift talked with everyone, shaking hands, asking questions, and laughing at jokes. Sometimes he spoke English, sometimes Japanese.

"He just seems to know who wants to speak Japanese and who wants to speak English," Mari murmured to me.

I glanced at her. I knew that look on her face. Mari was making a plan.

My parents had questions for Father Swift. We learned that he was a Maryknoll missioner. That group, or order, of priests, brothers and sisters worked in many parts of the world.

"We are delighted there is a Catholic church here, " Mom was saying. "You have a nice choir."

"Yes, but no organist," Father Swift said.

"But I see there is a small organ," Mari said. "I could play it."

Father Swift looked delighted. "Good!"

"And would you teach me to speak Japanese?"

"Yes, of course." Father Swift obviously took this just-turned sixteen-year old seriously.

"Thank you. When can we start?" she asked.

Mari never " beat around the bush."

"Tomorrow we start your lessons at your place, if that works for your family," he said. "And choir practice happens right here, Tuesday evenings."

It was not long before a large blackboard was put up on the wall of our kitchen. Mari covered it with Japanese letters and words. Father Swift was an excellent teacher and she was a quick learner.

The rest of us did not learn so easily. The Japanese alphabet was so different from what we knew. But Mari was soon writing short sentences.

The next day we drove into the town of Granada. Before Dad started working, we had some business to attend to.

We needed to open an account at a local bank. We also needed groceries. Our barracks had a kitchen, unlike most of the other barracks.

"Let's get a big bag of potatoes," Mari said.

Mom looked at her a little questioningly, but she didn't say no.

And lastly, we all wanted to go to the drug store to buy some magazines. We hadn't brought much to read in Amache. Besides, the best way to learn about world events and news was by reading, as we did not have a radio.

"And toothpaste. Help me remember we need toothpaste!" Mom said.

We were all in good moods. It was fun arriving in a town that was new to us. We didn't know we were about to experience what many of the Japanese-Americans coped with all the time.

While the others headed to the grocery store, I went with Dad into the bank.

We walked up to the bank teller.

"Good morning," Dad greeted her. "I'd like to open an account, please."

Given that bank accounts are a big part of a bank's business, we didn't expect any problems.

The teller wore a dark blue dress with tiny yellow flowers on it. I admired the lace collar. She looked up over her glasses and studied first Dad and then me.

"Are you new in town?" she asked.

I felt funny. Her voice held no friendliness.

"Yes," Dad answered breezily. "Just got here, and need to have a bank account!"

I thought he sounded pleasant and friendly, but she looked at him with narrowed eyes.

"Are you working at that camp?" she asked, her voice low.

I felt a sort of tightness in my stomach. Dad, however, remained relaxed.

"Yes, at the relocation center."

"We don't give accounts to people from the camp." Her voice was flat.

"Well, everyone needs to have a bank account, and this is the only bank in town," Dad said. "I hope you will accommodate me."

"We don't give accounts to people from the camp," she repeated in the same flat voice but louder. And this time I saw a look in her eyes that said, "Don't even try to ask again."

A door behind her opened up and a man stepped out from what was probably his office.

"Is there a problem, Miss Morgan?" he asked.

Quickly Dad spoke, directing his words to the man, "We are here to open an account."

"He's from the camp," Miss Morgan said.

"We don't give accounts to people from the camp," the man said.

Had they practiced saying that?

Dad stood there silently for a moment, just looking at the man.

I held my breath.

"You are in the banking business, correct?" Dad said. His voice remained level.

"We don't want your business," Miss Morgan said.

Dad did not move right away. I think he was trying to decide what to do next. But the man had no problems in deciding.

He came around the counter and headed to the door. He opened it and stood aside of it, waiting for us to leave.

"Good day to you, sir," he said. Clearly, we were being dismissed.

Dad gave me a quick look as if to say, "Just follow me."

We walked out of that bank, never to return.

"Well, that is the coldest "good day to you" I have ever gotten," Dad muttered.

At the car, we found Mom, Larry and Mari putting groceries into the trunk. Mari was hoisting a 10-pound bag of potatoes in.

"Any problems at the grocery store?" Dad asked Mom. I thought he sounded a little worried.

"No. Why? Did you have trouble at the bank?" she asked, slamming the trunk shut.

"Oh, a bit. It seems our money, earned through Amache, is not welcome at the bank."

Mari and Larry looked at me. "They were kind of nasty to us," I said, "and wouldn't let Dad open an account."

"Well, we can figure that out later. Right now, let's go to the drug store," Mom said cheerfully, and led us down the street.

We had to walk past the bank to get to the drug store. I looked into the window. Miss Morgan looked up from her work. Our eyes met and she again gave me that narrowed look, as if I were disgusting.

I wanted to stick my tongue out at her. She certainly deserved it. But I was 12 now and could stop myself from that kind of action. I knew she did not approve of my father's work, but I knew he was doing what was right.

Sometimes just knowing you are doing the right thing is enough.

At the drug store, Mom got the toothpaste.

"I don't see any magazines anywhere," I said, having perused the whole store.

"Well, there was a war on. We have to do without a lot of things," Mom said.

We headed towards the door, but Mari said she wanted to look for something. She'd catch up with us.

When she did, she had a story for us: a woman had gone up to the counter soon after we had left the store. She asked for a copy of "Good Housekeeping" magazine. The clerk reached under the counter, where he quickly located one.

"Here you go, Mrs. Larkin. We have to keep the magazines under the counter now. We sell them only to the locals," he said and took her money.

We all got into the car, Larry mumbling sarcastically that this was "one friendly town."

That night in bed, I punched my pillow a few times. That didn't help me relax, so I sat up and put on the light. Mari was still in the other room.

Mom must have noticed, for a few minutes later there was a soft knock on my door and she looked in. "Can't sleep?"

My answer was an angry question. "Why are some people so mean to others?"

Mom came and sat down next to me on the bed. "It is very complicated because humans are very complicated. We will talk more about this situation, but not right now. I don't think that would help you go to sleep."

She reached for my hand. "Since the world began there has been good and evil," she said softly.

I thought of the many renditions of the story of Adam and Eve and their fall from grace, and then their sons, the one who was good, the one who was bad. But that was not what my mother was thinking about.

"When I see evil in the world and feel angry or helpless, I think about people I know who are doing good. I also like to remember people in the past who stood up to injustice."

It was so nice having Mom close. I put my head on her shoulder.

"Helen, do you know the story of your ancestor, Thomas Duffy?"

I sat upright again. "No!" I said. I was a little irked that here was another family story I hadn't heard—that happens to the youngest child, I guess. But I was also very intrigued. "Tell me!"

"Thomas Duffy was my great-great-grandfather who—"

"Then he was my great-great-great grandfather!" I marveled. It was very hard to imagine someone who was related to me that lived so long ago.

"Thomas Duffy and his brother were teachers in Ireland. This was around the 1830s, over 100 years ago. For many years there had been unfair laws that kept the Catholics of the country from owning much or earning much. These laws made it very difficult for Catholics to practice their religion, too. The laws were also about education: there could not be any Catholic schools or even any Catholic teachers."

I looked at Mom, expecting an explanation from her.

"There are many reasons why people take power over others, Helen. And over the centuries, different groups take power for a while. Then things change and others take over. Sometimes they are better and sometimes worse than the group they replaced," she said. "And it is always more involved than it first appears. For example, at this time in Ireland, the Presbyterians were being persecuted too."

Mari walked in. She had a big book in her hands. Clearly she had overheard what Mom was telling me, and had come to add to the information. Had she brought that book with her from home? It looked like a history book. She never ceased to amaze me.

She sat down on the bed too and said, "I read in here about a man named Edmund Burke. He lived about the same time as these laws you are talking about. They were called the Penal Laws. He wrote that these Penal Laws were so very clever that they were able to keep a whole group of people so oppressed, their dignity was taken from them. So, Mom, is that is what is happening now to the Japanese-Americans?"

Mom was silent for a few moments and then said, "Well, yes. I guess that might be a good description."

Now I got impatient. "What about this Thomas Duffy?"

Mom nodded. "Well, despite these laws, most Irish parents, wanted their children taught by Irish teachers, who were mostly Catholic. Thomas Duffy and his brother were Catholic so they had to teach secretly."

"Wow," I said, thinking of the classrooms filled with noisy kids I had been in. I wondered how anyone could teach secretly.

"They actually taught in ditches and behind bushes or hedges. These were called 'hedge schools,'" Mom explained and then paused to yawn. "I think some 'hedge' schools were also held in cow houses, mud cabins or buildings made of sod."

Mari shuttered. "Those must have been wet and cold places."

"And smelly," I added. "Dark, too."

Mom nodded. "One child was always on guard, watching for anyone who would report them, for these teachers were considered criminals."

"Criminals! They were actually good people who were teachers," Mari said.

"What would happen if they were caught?"

"The police, or whatever they were called then, would sort of hunt for the teachers. When someone was caught, they'd be put in prison. So they were always in hiding.

"They had to rely on families to feed and hide them. And these families were terribly poor—mainly because of these laws. Often teachers were paid with things like butter instead of money."

I imagined what it would be like to be the kid who was on guard. I'd pretend to just be playing, but always keep looking around and listening. I tried to picture this great-great-great grandfather of mine, not as an elderly man, but as a young person, teaching and worrying he'd be caught. He must have been scared the whole time!

"How could anyone teach secretly?" I wondered out loud.

"And how could kids learn?" Mari said. "They must have been scared too, and cold, maybe hungry."

Mom nodded but said, "I think they did learn, though. These teachers were well-educated people. I have read that they taught Latin, Greek, arithmetic, reading and writing."

I was thinking that this ancestor of mine was quite the hero. "What happened to Thomas and his brother?"

"The brothers eventually had to leave Ireland and live undercover because they knew they would soon be captured otherwise," Mom said. "For three generations, the family did not use the name Duffy. It took that long before it was safe to use."

Mom looked at me and smiled a weak smile. "Well, Helen, I had hoped that we could have a nice comforting talk so you would go to sleep, but it was hardly that."

Mari seemed lost in her own thoughts, but I had to yawn. "I am tired, now, though, Mom. And I am glad to learn about this great-great-great grandfather who really was a 'great' person too!"

Mom kissed me on my forehead, said good night, and led Mari, whose nose was back in the book, out of the room. I turned out the light.

I think I fell asleep pretty quickly, but I had many dreams of sitting behind bushes, and in damp ditches, trying to memorize Latin words. There was a vague person in these dreams, who I couldn't really see. But even in the dream, I knew he was a brave man, trying to do good in a world gone bad.

Mari came home from choir practice on Tuesday evening in an energetic mood.

"Father Swift asked me if I would help prepare a little girl for her First Communion," she announced. "Of course I said yes. He said he'd stop over in a little while with some books to work on with her."

Mom looked up from the shirt she was ironing and nodded. "Dad should be here soon, too. Larry, could you put water on for tea?"

"Father Swift said he'd try to arrange it so I can go over to her house tomorrow. Oh, and I ran into Mollie and Edna, the girls I met our first day here. They are coming over in a couple of days, OK?"

"Of course," Mom said.

"We are going to make French fried potatoes," Mari said.

Mom laughed. "Of course," she said.

"So that's why you wanted that big bag of potatoes," Larry commented.

Mari nodded and laughed. "And you can eat as many as you can cook, Larry! Helen, do you want to come with me to little Mikiko's house? You can meet her family and just hang out while I work with her."

"Sure!" I said. I did want to meet more kids and to see the other parts of the camp.

When Father Swift knocked on the door, Mari let him in. Mom set the steaming teapot on the table while Larry set out the extra chair so we could all enjoy Father Swift's visit.

"I ran into some of the choir members on my way over here," Father Swift said, accepting a cup from Mom. "They are delighted to have an organist and they enjoyed meeting you, Mari."

Mari grinned and said, "Well, then we have a good exchange, Japanese lessons for music at Mass!"

He had the books for Mari. They went over some pages, for he needed to explain to Mari things he especially wanted the child to understand.

I thought of my own First Communion. What would it be like to celebrate such a special day when you had to live in a prison?

Just then Dad walked in. More tea was poured as Dad loosened his tie and sat down.

"How was your first day?" Mom asked Dad.

He shook his head. "It will take me a few days to understand all the problems. I couldn't begin to explain right now," he said, and then addressed Father Swift. "But I would like to know what brought you here."

"I worked for several years in the northern part of Korea, called Pyongyang. When I came back to the United States, one of my jobs was working with Japanese-Americans in Los Angeles. Soon after the attack on Pearl Harbor, we began hearing about the government forcing all the Japanese-Americans living on the West Coast into these centers. I volunteered to go with them."

Wow, I thought. He had been here for about four years now!

But Larry had a one-word question. "Why?

"Well, I already knew many of the people who would be moved. I understood the situation they were in. And I speak Japanese," he said. "I realized pretty quickly that the people forced to come here would need a great deal of spiritual help and comfort. "

Dad nodded. Then he said, almost as if he were talking to himself, "What do you think it would feel like to have your own government betray you?"

Larry looked at Dad, quizzically.

So Dad explained, "Our government just turned against them, saying they were evil! People no different from you and me! The government claimed they needed to lock up these 'evil' people so they couldn't do bad things."

Father Swift answered Dad's question, "I think this hurts the Japanese people very deeply because of their cultural background."

Mari was frowning with intense concentration, but it was Mom who spoke, asking, "Do you think they take it to heart and have almost started to believe that it must be true, if those in authority are saying it?"

Now it was Father Swift who seemed deep in thought. Slowly at first, he explained, "There are many cultures within America. The way I see it, the Japanese culture tends to have great respect for authority. So when the authority—in this case, the federal government—says they are bad, people in that culture start to question themselves, particularly when the situation forced on them is so extreme."

I think I was looking back and forth between each person who was talking, as if I were watching a Ping-Pong tournament. Like Mari, I was working very hard to understand all this.

Father Swift set his teacup on the table and went on, "Those of us with different cultural experiences might just say, 'You're wrong, I know who I am!' We would not brood over it. But my experience with the Japanese culture has led me to believe it is not only that they were forced out of their homes, schools, work—from their whole lives, actually. It is also this questioning of their integrity."

I glanced at Mom. She understood my silent question and said quietly, "Their honesty, their truthfulness, their self-respect."

Father Swift smiled at me and then turned to Larry. "To answer your question of why I came here voluntarily, my work is to go where I am needed and to do what I can. I feel God calls me to do this work.

"And the way I see this work is that the people here need to know that even if their government has betrayed them, God and the Church are still at their side.

"I feel God wants them to hear His message of 'You are not bad.' This is what I am trying to tell them: You are a good person who is being treated very badly by people in power. God loves you and He knows what is happening and He won't abandon you. Trust Him and have faith. People have gone through bad times before."

The teapot was empty, but the adults kept talking. I was getting sleepy, though, and went off to bed.

The next day, Mari gathered up the books from Father Swift and we set off. We were going to enter the largest part of the camp. Not even Dad had been there yet, despite his job.

We passed the white cottages of the staff, tucked inside the cheerful picket fence and perched on green grass. Of course, we had left our own quarters, which were not so pretty, but had a modern kitchen and three bedrooms.

And we stepped into a world of desolation.

Despite the acres of farmland tended so successfully by people in Amache, the center was mainly made up of barracks. Row after endless row of colorless, rectangular buildings.

These were broken up only by the small areas between buildings. Those were like alleys in a city, but were just strips of dirt and sand.

I quickly realized that when a wind passed through these alleys, the dust and sand rose into the air. I closed my eyes against this.

Mari coughed a little and then said, "Wow—it would be hard to play outside in this area when it is windy."

"And I think it is usually windy," I said.

Mari looked around. "Helen, help me figure out how to find the number to Mikiko's place."

After a couple of minutes of looking, it was Mari who figured out where we needed to go to get to the right section of barracks.

My thoughts had taken a different path. I said, "At first I felt like this was such a horrible place, and it is, but there are good things too."

My sister paused from her number searching. "Yes—the sound of kids playing, even if I don't see them, does make it seem less dreadful! Thanks for pointing that out, Helen!"

"I've noticed some sort of gardens too," I said and as we moved between the ends of two barracks and looked down the alley the buildings made, I saw another. Someone had created a low fence by placing large stones around a small area. Within it some vegetables and flowers were growing. Red, yellow and orange flowers, against the no-color barracks and the dull dirt.

Mari smiled. I resolved to make a small garden here too.

In the distance I saw that someone had made a playground by creating a teeter-totter and a couple of swings.

Down the next alley, we saw a makeshift clothesline hung with diapers. The breeze caught them, and they flapped like sails on a ship. They would dry quickly in the wind and heat.

"I don't know why, but clothes hanging on lines always makes me feel cheerful," Mari remarked. "A funny thing to cheer a person up!"

Yet, I knew what she meant.

The sound of children at play got louder, and soon we were seeing little groups of toddlers outside, supervised by grandparents, a solitary little girl singing to a doll, a bunch of grubby little boys digging in the dirt, and then a game of basketball without a basket.

More gardens, more laundry, more play, within this community of ramshackle housing.

I had recently read that word 'ramshackle' and really liked it—and it fit here, among these quickly built barracks.

Finally, Mari and I found the area that contained the quarters of Mikiko's family. We turned to walk down an alley of sand and dirt.

I think that is when it hit me. We had walked by buildings marked "toilets" and others labeled "showers." Did this mean there were no bathrooms in the apartments the families lived in?

"Mari!" I said in a whisper. I didn't want to embarrass anyone who could hear me. "Do the families here have to share not only a shower room but sinks and toilets too?"

She paused and looked around. "I suppose so. I don't know, I guess. We'll find out soon enough, at Mikiko's house."

I was sort of horrified. "Do you think they were used to that before they came?" I asked. I was trying to imagine what it would be like to suddenly have to share a bathroom with strangers.

"I think most of the people here have houses just like we have in Chicago. So, no, I don't suppose they were any more used to this than we would be."

We looked at each other. It was bothering her as much as it was bothering me.

But Mari was like a beach ball that couldn't be kept underwater.

"Well, come on," she said determinedly. "All the more reason to meet this family and be kind to them. It's not their fault they are here."

"Just whose fault is it?"

Mari did not answer right away. Then she said, "The government, I suppose. That's who issued the order making all these people come here. And then there is fear. A lot of non-Japanese people just got so scared after the attack by Japan on Pearl Harbor, they let this happen."

We were getting close to the right number. Sounds of family life came from each barrack.

They have no privacy, I thought. Any sounds floated outside and probably right into the connected apartment too.

I realized Mari was still talking about what had caused this injustice.

"And besides fear, there is something else. I don't know what it is in humans, but people can hate other people just because they are different in some way. So it is the fault of evil in the world, and the people who give into it....if that makes any sense."

I nodded. I sort of understood. Things like this are very complicated and usually involve both bad feelings and closed feelings.

"Here we are, I think," Mari said. We knocked on a door. A pretty woman answered, a warm smile on her face. "You've come to teach Mikiko?" she asked.

"Yes, I'm Mari, and here is my sister, Helen."

"I am Emi Naya. Come in! Mikiko is waiting for you! She's really looking forward to meeting you!" she said and stepped aside.

She stepped aside, I thought, just like the mean banker had done to get Dad and me to leave a few days before. Here, though, we were being welcomed.

A little girl about 7-years-old, with a long, dark ponytail, was grinning and looking excitedly at Mari. Mari leaned over and said, "Hello, Mikiko! I am so happy you are going to make your First Communion. It is such a special event! Do you know why?"

Mari was already teaching and she hadn't even sat down yet! Mikiko took Mari's hand and led her to a table.

"Please, sit down," Mrs. Naya said to me.

I looked around. There were two sets of bunk beds built against the wall, just a few feet from the table. It seemed she expected me to sit on one of the bottom beds, so I did. There really wasn't anywhere else to sit.

I smiled at her to thank her and looked around. One wall was all shelving. On the open shelving, I saw neatly folded clothing and towels, some books and papers, and a few very small toys. Some of the cupboards had doors.

A vase of flowers made of colorful paper rested on the table, and curtains hung over the window. Everything was very close together for it was a small room. A blanket hung from a clothesline, cutting off part of the room. There was no sink that I could see. A pot bellied stove, which was not in use since it was July. And a single light bulb hung down from the ceiling. I saw no other lamps.

Mrs. Naya saw me looking around. I felt a little embarrassed. "You have a nice–" I hesitated and then said feebly, "house."

She smiled at me. "Thank you. My father-in-law is a carpenter. He has made our place very nice."

That gave me some courage. "How many are there in your family?"

"My husband's parents, my husband and I and our three children."

That was two more people than in my family. I wondered how much more space there was beyond the blanket-curtain. And at that moment, I heard the giggles of small children behind it.

Quietly, so as not to disturb Mari and Mikiko at the table, Mrs. Naya explained, "My younger children are with my mother-in-law in the other room."

Soon I would realize the "other room" was a space behind the curtain just big enough for another bed. This was their whole "house!" No bathroom here.

"She is trying to keep the little ones quiet, but, well, you know how small children are," said Mrs. Naya.

One little face, cute as a button, peeked around the edge of the curtain. An even smaller one then appeared.

Mari looked up from where she and Mikiko were reading. She chuckled a little and suggested, "Helen, would you like to take the kids outside? Would that be all right, Mrs. Naya?"

I heard little squeals of delight from behind the curtain. "Yes," she said, smiling. In a minute I met the grandmother, and 5-year-old Itsuo and his little sister, Tomomi. Each child took my hand and we stepped outside.

Immediately I wondered what in the world I was going to do with these kids. There was no yard, of course, just this strip of dirt between the barracks. The playground I had seen was too far for me to walk the children.

I guessed they had no toys. Where would they have put them?

"Let's sing a song!" I suggested, a little desperately. So we sang. They knew lots of kids' songs, like "Twinkle, Twinkle, Little Star."

Itsuo sang gustily and tiny Tomomi plugged along as well as she could.

"I can sing 'Mary Had a Little Lamb,'" Itsuo said proudly, so of course, I invited him to do so. I sat down on the one step in front of the door and patted it to invite Tomomi to sit next to me.

"We are the audience now," I explained to her.

Tomomi studied me with serious dark eyes. I don't think she had any idea of what an audience was, but she seemed to understand to sit next to me. She plopped down and sat there, very solemnly.

Itsuo, on the other hand, understood completely. He stood up proudly in front of us as if composing himself before singing in a concert hall.

He was wearing bib overalls and a checkered shirt. And when he bowed politely to us, I thought he was just about the cutest little kid I have ever seen!

He cleared his throat, which delighted me, and began singing, "Mary had a little lamb, little lamb, little lamb....."

When he finished, I led Tomomi in a rousing round of applause. She enjoyed that.

But Itsuo wasn't finished yet. He cleared his throat again and began singing the same song in Japanese.

This time, Tomomi started the applause before I did. We were cheering and clapping, and Itsuo was bowing and bowing when I glanced up and noticed their grandmother looking out the window at us. I think she had tears in her eyes.

By now, Tomomi had found a stick, clearly left there from a walk they taken, for there wasn't a tree in this alleyway. She had an idea, so I watched. She began drawing in the dirt with it. Pretty soon, Itsuo produced another stick from underneath the step and we were all drawing with sticks or fingers.

"Hi," someone said.

I looked up from my dirt drawing and saw a girl about my age.

"Hi, Katherine!" Tomomi shouted and ran to hug her. Though she had been quite silent up till now, Tomomi said, "This is Helen, my friend!"

"Hi, Tomomi's friend Helen!" Katherine said, grinning.

Itsuo looked up from the airplane he was drawing. "Hey, Katherine, can we play with your brother's ball, please?"

"I'll ask. Come on," she said.

I glanced back at the window and saw Grandmother, who nodded. I had no idea how far we would be going and I didn't want to just go off with the kids. But I took this as permission.

I needn't have worried. Katherine lived only two doors down, in another small space with homemade furniture.

I was quickly introduced to her brother, Richard. He was about 10. It seemed he had brought two balls with him. One was a baseball and another a kickball. Soon we were all playing kickball in the bleak space between the barracks, laughing and shouting and, at least for a little while, not thinking about where we were or why we were there.

Mrs. Naya and Grandmother came outside to sit on the step to watch and talk. They were soon joined by adults from other apartments.

When Mari and Mikiko were finished with their first lesson, they joined us. We played, kicking the ball and running to makeshift bases, while little Tomomi just ran around us. The adults were smiling and laughing.

When it was time for us to leave, Mari said she would be back in two days for another session and promised to bring me again.

Itsuo and Tomomi hugged me. Katherine and Richard grinned and waved good-bye. Mari and I set off for our quarters, having made lots of friends.

I felt happy and excited and did not look up at the guard tower once.

A few hours later, Dad came home from work. Mom had made a simple supper of sandwiches, carrots, apple slices, milk and cake. We sat down together to eat.

"Dad, Helen and I have lots and lots to tell you!" Mari said. "We had a great day!"

He smiled and took a bite of his sandwich.

"Yes, the girls made many friends, young and not so young," Mom said. "But first, how was your day?"

"Well, I am coming to know the others who work in administration here," he said. "I'd say that the staff are here to do a specific job and to get paid for it."

Dad didn't sound as if he thought that was good or bad. Dad could be careful like that, trying not to judge.

Then he said, "So tell me all about what you girls learned today!"

A lively discussion followed!

My father came home the next day to the sound of laughter and the smell of frying potatoes.

He stood in the doorway, watching and smiling at our kitchen antics for a minute, greeted everyone and then went into a bedroom. He worked very hard all day and probably wanted some quiet.

At least we had bedrooms, I thought. Katherine and Richard's family's space was perhaps a fourth the size we had.

Mollie and Edna and Mari were taking turns at the stove, monitoring the potato sticks sizzling in oil. When not at the stove, they scrubbed and sliced more potatoes. And talked.

I was in on it, as was Larry. As soon as a batch cooled off, we all ate them. So the scrubbing, slicing and frying went on for some time!

So did the conversation.

"Why are you here?" Mollie asked. "We were forced here, but you came here voluntarily. Why in the world would your parents bring you here?"

Larry and I let Mari take that one.

We both knew that Dad had said, "I can do more good as a lawyer in the centers as they are closing than I can at my old job at Chicago Title and Trust. Less money, of course, but I can't just do a 'regular job' when American citizens have been imprisoned without ever being accused of a crime—or given a trial or been convicted!"

I went over all the thoughts I had already had about this: Dad could have gone back to the job he had had before the war. If he had done that, we would have lived in our comfortable house near Chicago. But it was Dad's desire to be of service that brought us here, and now we were having experiences I was already enjoying.

But while I thought about Dad's beliefs, Mari talked about Mom.

"Well, maybe if I tell you what my Mom did during the Depression, you will see why my parents brought us here. You know, during the Depression, everyone was poor."

Mollie nodded and Edna, snatching up a French fry, said, "And many were hungry."

"Lots of men were forced to leave their families, wandering all over in hopes of finding work somewhere. And they were hungry," Mari said. "Mom always fed anyone who came to the backdoor.

"And she told us kids that these people were good, hardworking men down on their luck. Often at dinnertime, she fed half the neighborhood kids who just appeared at our door as if they had been dropped off by their guardian angels!"

Mari tossed another handful of sliced potatoes into the hot fat in the frying pan. Ah, that intense sizzling sound that happens when the potatoes hit the hot oil!

As they fried more quietly, Mari said, "Our mother feels called to help others. She also has an enormous trust in God. She believes strongly in the power of prayer."

I wondered if Mollie and Edna understood that my parents actually felt that it was God who was calling them to be here.

Mom kept in touch with that call by praying. Right now, with the kind of work she and Dad were doing, I figured Mom's belief in the power of prayer had her beating on the doors in heaven of all her favorite saints–and doing so with both fists!

Then Mari pulled this latest batch of French fries out of the hot oil. Even though we had all eaten a lot already, my mouth was watering!

"We'll be too full to go to the mess hall at dinner time," Edna said, happily.

"Not the best place to eat," Larry agreed.

Mollie nodded. "It is noisy and crowded. I know my mother misses our family dinners. She loves to cook and she loves to gather her family around the table at home...."

Her voice trailed off, but in my mind her words seemed to go "bam!"

I suddenly got it: for Mollie's family, there were no more dinners in their home. No more making and eating food they wanted to eat.

I knew from my time at the Naya's barrack that there was no kitchen, particularly no stove. And, I supposed, they could not have brought dishes and pots and pans here.

Maybe Larry was thinking the same thing because he asked, "How long has your family been here?"

"More than three years," Edna said quietly.

"Man, you must miss so much!" Larry said.

Both Edna and Mollie looked at him. They seemed to be grateful to Larry for just recognizing what they were coping with every day.

This encouraged me to pipe up.

"I was in a family's barracks yesteday—Mari and I went. They had a table and chairs and beds, shelves and cupboards. Mrs. Naya had said her father-in-law had 'made it nice.' Did she mean he had made the furniture and cupboards?"

"Probably," said Mollie. "Everything anyone has in their place they most likely had to make themselves."

"So no one brought any furniture here?"

"Oh, no—we were only allowed to bring what we could carry, one suitcase. "

We were all silent for a short time, thinking about this. You can't carry a bed or a table or even a warm quilt.

"Did the government provide you with anything in terms of your living space?" Larry asked quietly.

"Each place had a little stove for heating, not cooking, and one lightbulb that hung down from the ceiling," Mollie said.

Edna added, "They had some bedframes. And would you believe they gave us sacks of some fabric and straw to stuff these sacks with!"

"For what—not mattresses!" Larry was horrified.

"Yes, mattresses, if you can call them that. But they didn't give us anything else. Nothing. There was a lot of scrap lumber left over from building the barracks. We were told it was not for the taking, but it was just sitting there and everyone needed furniture! So everybody took it...we were already in prison, so taking something we really needed to be able to survive in here seemed fair," Mollie said. "Fortunately, my dad and uncle are pretty handy. Edna helped a lot too, and together they built some shelves, tables and some chairs."

"And Mollie's and my bunk bed. It would take up too much space for all the beds to be on the floor," Edna said.

"Helen said the family she visited had seven people in a pretty small space," Larry said. "How many people are there in your family?"

"Six—which means we are pretty crowded, but you have to have more than seven people to get a bigger place," Mollie said.

"How did you decide what to bring?" Mari asked.

Mollie just sighed.

Edna answered, "It was very confusing. We didn't know where we were going or for how long. So we had no idea what kind of weather we would have—many people didn't bring enough warm clothes. We just didn't have any information.

"Plus, we only had a very short time to get ready to leave. We couldn't leave anything in our home because we were afraid someone would steal it when we were gone. My parents packed up important papers and our photographs and put them in a bank box.

"Our dishes and most of our clothes are being stored at our neighbor's house. We gave away other things."

I didn't know what to say, but Edna went on.

"We were some of the first families to get here. The camp wasn't finished yet. My grandfather found out there had been a lot of things that caused this. This WRA and the government had disagreements, and then there were labor strikes by some of the contractors. I don't know who all these people were, but they weren't ready for us to come—as if we wanted to, either!

"There were only two blocks of barracks built before we arrived. There was one mess hall—one! There were maybe 1,000 people here! We had to eat in shifts—there were three or four shifts for every meal.

"And get this: one bathroom."

I must have looked horrified, because I certainly felt that way!

And Edna still had one more outrageous fact to add, "If we wanted to get cleaned up, like take a shower, or just get some water to bring to our barracks, we had to walk and walk and walk...."

"It's a crime," Larry said. "It's outrageous."

I guess that is what Edna needed one of us to say. She breathed a sigh of relief.

Mollie had remained silent and now she chopped a few more potatoes. Her shiny black hair covered the side of her face from the rest of us.

Then, in a quiet voice, she said, "We had to give away Skippy."

Even though they had not spoken of Skippy before, Mari, Larry and I all knew immediately that Skippy was their dog.

I felt a little bit like I had been punched in the stomach.

No one spoke for a few minutes. There was just the sound of the knife on the cutting board.

Edna and Mollie left, having eaten too many French fries to need to go to the mess hall. A little while later, Dad joined the rest of us for glasses of lemonade and talk.

"Are there gatherings for everyone here, like dances, dinners, or other celebrations?" Mom asked Dad.

"I haven't heard of anything like that," he said. "I doubt there are any kinds of gatherings for everyone to do together. I think the staff people, for the most part, keep pretty separate from everyone else. I have heard them use the term 'the colony' to refer to the part of the camp where the internees live."

He and Mom exchanged meaningful looks.

Larry and I looked to Mari for an explanation. So often she questioned our parents, and Larry and I then learned something we wanted to know. And that is exactly what happened now.

" A colony," Mari mused. "Like the original 13 states were colonies of England?"

Mom nodded.

"And a colony is not free, but must do what the controlling country wants?"

Dad nodded.

"But this camp isn't really a colony," Larry said. "We are all still in the United States, which is a free country."

"Yes, but I think the staff people use that term as a symbol. Colonists are often looked down upon by the country in charge," Dad said, adding, "and the internees aren't really free here."

I knew they were not free, but I suddenly wondered about citizens in a free country. I felt really confused. "I thought you said that most of the people here are American citizens. But am I wrong—are the people here not citizens?"

"You were correct—most of the people here are citizens. They were born here, just as you and I were," Mom said. "You may find that some of the grandparents, and a few of the parents, were born in Japan. But that does not make them people who should be imprisoned."

"Why haven't they become citizens yet?" I asked, still very confused.

"Because there was a law made in 1790 that says Asian people not born in the United States cannot become citizens," Dad said.

Larry whistled and shook his head, saying, "That is over 150 years ago!!!"

I admired his ability to do the arithmetic so quickly.

"In school I learned that the words to the national anthem were written in 1814," Larry said. "We have been singing "the land of the free and the home of the brave" for a long time. But I never thought about it being only for certain people. I'll never sing that song again without thinking about the excluded people." He paused and then added, "Maybe I'll never sing it again, period."

Mari said with determination, "Well, there may be ways to exclude and imprison certain people, but right here, right now, there is something I can do about it."

She had that look on her face we all knew. Mari was scheming.

We let her scheme. She'd tell us about it when she was ready.

I went to bed before Mari, and lay awake in the summer twilight. I found myself thinking about my dollhouse. It had been a gift made by my grandfather the year before he died. He had not only made the dollhouse but the tiny furniture. Mom had called it a labor of love.

Now I could feel Grandpa's love, every time I saw the dollhouse. I could feel it, even now.

I missed him and wondered where he was. I believed he was with God, but what was that like?

The next morning, Dad went off to work and Larry, having found out there was a baseball league, had gone off to find out where he could sign up.

Mom was off somewhere. Mari and I had finished up the breakfast dishes and Mari was writing Japanese sentences on the blackboard.

There was a knock at the door. It was Edna, hoping to borrow a book.

We were all talking when Mom came into the house, her arms full of laundry. We had wondered where she was.

"Whose clothes are those?" Mari asked. "They're mostly white!"

Anyone who could avoid wearing white would do so in this place of dust and sand.

"This is the 'sacred wash'," Mom quipped. "I told Father Swift we could do the church laundry."

Edna looked at her curiously. "Mrs. Hannan, what do you mean by church laundry? It is a building! How can a building have laundry?"

Mom laughed. "The altar cloth, some of Father's vestments and all the little white cloths used for Mass, such as the purificator for wiping the chalice–things like that."

I had a feeling I would be roped into that, and I was right.

In the afternoon I noticed my mother bringing out 'the box.' Wherever we went, such as to a new army base, Mom brought along this old cardboard box. And, like a magician she pulled the most amazing stuff out of it.

No matter what was needed she would improvise something that would do. She sewed beautifully. She had made Mari a prom dress last spring out of a bunch of old curtains and Mari had looked lovely.

"So what are you going to magically create now, Mom?" I asked.

She smiled at me, appreciating the compliment.

As she rummaged through it, she said, "Well, Mari is preparing that little girl for her First Communion, so she will need a special dress....and perhaps a wreath of some sort, for her hair...."

I could tell she was lost in thoughts and plans, so I left her to it. But I wasn't surprised when, an hour later, I saw some white cloth that had been freshly ironed. Now it was laid out on the table. And Mom was happily cutting out a little dress.

Mari came to see what was going on.

"Oh, Mom, Mikiko will be so happy when she sees this!" Mari said, giving Mom a big hug.

"Well," Mom said, scissors in hand. "She must have something beautiful for this important day. It will help her understand just how special and important it is!"

My mother had a "down-to-earth" way of combining the spiritual parts of life with the practical things. She never separated them. Mikiko was about to have a spiritual celebration. So Mom figured she needed a new dress and made one.

That evening, Dad came home. He looked very tired, but I could tell he was also really agitated.

He had taken this job only knowing he would be helping Japanese-Americans who had been forced to leave their lives behind more than three years ago. Now, I guessed, he had a better understanding of what kind of help they needed from him.

Mom, always observant, said simply, "Tell us what is going on."

He sat down, as if he were weighed down with what he had to say.

"These people had two days' notice to walk away from their lives. Two days! They could bring only what they could fit in one suitcase—with no idea of the climate of the place they were being sent to. And in those two days, everything had to be dealt with —house and everything in it, car, their work, maybe a store, a business, a profession, a farm with growing crops and animals. You couldn't even take your pet."

I wanted to ask what happened to their pets, but the conversation moved too swiftly.

"They couldn't sell their stuff?" Larry asked.

Again I thought of my dollhouse, which I would never sell, no matter what!

"There was no time for that. But, even worse, given how fast everything was happening, who would buy anything? Why buy something when all you had to do was to wait two days for the families to leave and then walk into these houses and take what you want," Dad said grimly.

"You mean you think people are just stealing things?" Mari asked.

Dad nodded.

"Do you think others may have even moved into empty houses?" Mom asked softly.

"I think that is very likely. And I don't know how many of the people forced to come here will have any way of getting those homes back again," Dad said. "The government made no attempt to secure or safeguard any of the things that had to be left behind. I don't think it entered their mind to even think about trying to protect them."

There was a moment of quiet as we were mulling this over.

Then Dad went on. "I think there are about 120,000 people locked up in these so-called camps."

Mom and Mari both gasped. I struggled to imagine that huge number.

Larry repeated it, "One hundred and twenty thousand people!"

"And those in charge of gathering and forcing all those people into these prison camps were unbelievably thorough," Dad said. "Anyone with a drop of Japanese blood was locked up. In fact, I was told that they scooped up babies from three orphanages, two in Los Angeles and one in San Francisco. Orphaned children!

"There is a rumor that in one of the camps there is a little boy with curly red hair who is one thirty-second Japanese. Now I don't know if this is true, but the way they are rounding up everyone I can almost believe it."

"Where are these orphaned children now?" Mari asked.

"How can little kids be any kind of threat?" I asked, anger brewing inside of me.

"Where are these children now?" Mari repeated.

Dad said he didn't know. "At work today, I got talking with a staff person who was one of the first to arrive here. Apparently, the center was not finished before the first evacuees were forced to leave their homes and come here. The West Coast Defense Command refused to change the schedule, though, so they were put on trains and arrived here. What a disaster that was!"

"Edna told us about that! She and her family were some of the first people here. They didn't have enough bathrooms or mess halls or places to sleep!" I said.

Dad sighed and nodded. "It sounds like it was really terrible. Imagine being forced to leave everything you love, everything that made you feel safe, only to arrive on a train at night in a place that didn't have any lights set up yet.

"Families got off the train, arriving after dark. They had to stumble along, being led by others holding candles! Often adults and children fell into holes dug for new buildings."

I closed my eyes and imagined Edna and Mollie, carrying suitcases and trying to follow someone with just a candle to lead the way, through construction, dirt and uneven ground.

One candle in the immense darkness.

Dad had more to tell. "People slept in makeshift houses made of cardboard. The only light at night was by candles! There were so few bathhouses that just to get water, people had to walk several blocks. And the water supply for the camp was still inadequate and impure, so water was hauled in from the town....."

Again, silence. We were not usually a quiet family.

Once more I pictured Mollie and Edna, having to sleep in shacks made of cardboard. With candles for light! Talk about a fire hazard!

This was just not a problem of not being ready. This was cruel.

I wondered why neither Mollie nor Edna had told us how bad it really had been when they had arrived here.

Dad said, as much to himself as to us, "Those conditions—cardboard shelters, dangerous candles, bad water—that is just a complete disregard for human life. Our government doesn't see them as human beings. It sees them as dangerous creatures of no value who simply have to be kept alive."

I winced at the idea of little Mikiko and Edna as "creatures of no value."

Dad still needed to talk. "To tell the truth I don't think the government cared in the least how they were destroying these peoples' lives. Most of them will never again see anything they had to leave behind. Their past lives are gone as though some evil witch had waved a wand."

Then Mom asked him, "Are you sorry we came here?"

Dad gave her a smile that meant he knew she shared both his frustration and his mission.

"It would take Solomon himself to make things right for all these people. But I do think there is some value and comfort for the people just to know that someone knows and cares and is trying to help."

"Sometimes just trying to help is helping," Mari said.

Dad opened his arms and we all fell into them, in a comforting family hug.

It was a hot morning when Mari and I went off again to "the colony" for another lesson with Mikiko.

This time I looked up at the guard tower. I had counted the towers I had seen so far, and had gotten six. Larry was convinced there were more.

From my vantage point, the tower was set against the sky, which today was very blue and had big, rolling clouds. Of course, the ugly tower marred this sight.

It made me think of the time I found a dead bird. I was really young and didn't understand that the bird held still because it was dead. It was a lovely blue jay, whose colors might be the most "true" blue you could ever see! I bent over to look at the different shades of blue, along with the white. I was enjoying it, and suddenly I saw that there was a cut in the underside. I examined the innards I was able to see and shuddered at how that cut made the bird suddenly seem ugly.

Mari noticed my gaze. "I wonder what they are like," she said.

"Who?"

"The guards."

I looked again. It wasn't easy to see much of the one in this tower today, but it was obvious he had a gun and that he was watching us and everyone else. I thought he was wearing dark glasses.

"I wonder what it is like to have that job. He may not have wanted the job. Or maybe he did. He may not know any of the people in the barracks and wonder about then. He may dislike them. Or maybe he feels uncomfortable with what he has to do," she mused. Then she switched to her usual tone, "Let's walk another way than we did the other day."

This just meant walking through different sections of drab-color barracks set on sandy soil. I guess we were hoping to see if there was any relief to these endless, hopeless blocks.

I noticed a few young trees here and there. I knew my mother would have said they were probably planted in hope.

In hope of making this a better place? In hope that someday the planter would be back in a tree-filled place again?

We also saw a victory garden. It was bigger than the sweet, tiny plots I had seen the other day. But it was a garden, as compared to the acres of vegetables planted nearby. I knew victory gardens were planted to produce more food for people while our world was at war. In some countries, people had dug up their lawns and even tennis courts and rose gardens to turn them into gardens for vegetables, fruits and herbs. But this one, here in this windswept, dry place seemed to need its own victory. How could it survive? And yet, it was not only surviving but doing well!

I admired it and the gardeners who showed so much hope and resilience just by planting it, given the poor conditions. Like my mom making a special dress for Mikiko, these people were doing what they could to make things a little better. They weren't letting the bad circumstances defeat them.

Mari must have been thinking the same thing because she said," That little garden is a victory garden, really and truly, but not the way most people think of them!"

Then we saw another makeshift playground, with lots of kids shrieking on swings. And there was always laundry flapping in the wind outside of some barracks.

Now we had gotten to Mikiko's quarters. She and her mother greeted us warmly at their door. Itsuo and Tomomi peeked out from behind their mother. I knew what they wanted.

"Can I take the little ones outside, Mrs. Naya?" I asked. This time I had brought some crayons and paper with me.

Squealing with delight, Itsuo and Tomomi jumped down the little step in front of the door and Mikiko led Mari into the barracks. I heard Mari say, " I bet you'd like to draw a picture too, Mikiko. I am sure Helen will save a piece of paper for you!"

We sat on the ground, using the step as a table. I watched. I had intended to draw with them, but now I wanted to leave all the paper with them when we left.

I'd never seen little kids so happy to draw. Itsuo was amazing. He drew a picture of an airplane, with a million details on it. Then he added clouds and the sun. He must have decided the moon and some stars should be in the sky too. Carefully he drew those in. Little Tomomi seemed only able to draw lines and circles so far, but I noticed she was very thoughtful about which colors she chose. And she worked carefully to draw those lines and circles.

But the drawings were finished before Mari and Mikiko were done. I noticed Katherine and Richard returning to their quarters. They had been helping their mother with laundry.

Itsuo grinned. I already knew that grin—it meant he had an idea. "Richard, can we play kickball?"

Richard looked to his mother. She smiled and nodded. Richard and Katherine took the laundry into their place, and then joined us. Soon a rowdy game of kickball was causing the dust and sand to fly!

Our shouts and laughter brought out other kids and some adults and soon we had a small crowd.

A little while later, Mari and Mikiko came outside, hand in hand. I glanced at Mari. I could tell by the look on her face that, like Itsuo, she was hatching an idea. Probably the idea she had been working on last night.

As we walked back, she shared her idea with me: to invite all of these kids, no matter what their ages, to our house. It was so much bigger there, and we had a few games. Maybe we could get some toys. We already had crayons and paper. Richard could bring the balls.

And because Mari's ideas were usually good ones, and she never let a good idea get wasted, our house became a meeting place for many children.

Not many days passed before the "colony kids" were coming to our quarters every chance they got.

Sometimes it looked like a daycare center, with busy kids everywhere.

Katherine and others set up board games and played by the hour.

It turned out that Richard was quite the card shark. He taught lots of kids lots of games.

And Mom saw to it that there were always potatoes!

The kids all adored French fries and Mari and Edna and Mollie made them endlessly. Magically, every one of those French fries disappeared!

The 'sacred wash,' as we jokingly called the laundry from church, was of course, done by my family.

Our own clothing was washed by a woman named Setsuno. She lived in the barracks and earned money doing laundry for other families. Mom had hired her.

Setsuno took our dirty clothes to the shared laundry room. There was both hot and cold water there and a washing machine. After the clothes were clean, she would squeeze out the water using the wringer part of the machine. The clothes were still wet but not sopping wet. She would carry all those heavy clothes to our barracks and then hang them up. The only problem is that she always hung them up in the living room.

Mom would come home as Setsuno was finishing up. She had strung clotheslines all over that room. Each time, Mom tried to explain, "Please, Setsuno—hang the clothes outside or in the bedrooms! We have so little room and we really need to be able to walk and sit in this room!"

And every time, Setsuno looked at Mom with a very serious, honest face, and said, "Nail here, nail there, I hang."

I hadn't even noticed those nails in the flimsy walls of our quarters.

But that is the way it was, every single week! It got to be a joke in our family. When someone decided to do something that would take great determination and still may not work, someone else in the family would mutter, "Nail here, nail there, I hang."

But the sacred wash was different. In our barracks, Mom washed all the little white pieces that were used in different ways on the altar. These were sort of like towels, but a lot nicer. Sometimes she washed the altar cloth, too. All were hung up to dry. Then they had to be starched, which was putting a mixture on them to make them iron nicely and be smooth.

We may have had to make-do with a drafty barracks for our church, but we didn't have to have unkempt altar linens!

So said Mom.

On sunny days, Mom hung this wash outside. It dried quickly because it was always windy.

When she started to iron, I could hear the thump-thump of the iron on the ironing board.

Though Mari was busy learning Japanese, playing the portable organ, helping with choir practice, and supervising kids' games, she also did her share of housework.

One day she was ironing the altar cloth. It was a straight sheet of fabric, no tricky collars to press or buttons to go around, like one of Dad's shirts had. But it was linen and linen is beautiful but fussy. You have to have the iron pretty hot and even then, it is really hard to get rid of the wrinkles.

Now wrinkles might not seem like a big deal, but this was, after all, the biggest piece of cloth people saw when they came to Mass. Altar clothes were table clothes for the most important table of all tables.

But there was another reason for the ironing work too.

As Mari muttered a little about doing this tedious work, Mom said "We want it to be beautiful for the people who come to church. After all, they are forced to live far from all the things they treasure, in a drab and cheerless place. They can at least have a beautiful place to pray."

I hadn't thought of it that way.

And then I was assigned ironing of all the small cloths. I liked the sizzling sound of the hot iron hitting the little droplets of water on the fabric and the smell of the linen while it was damp and hot. Then I folded each square carefully, matching each corner to another and ironed it again. It gave me a little sense of satisfaction of a job well done.

Ironing wasn't the only skill I learned.

The first sewing I ever did was replacing the protective linen neckbands on Father Swift's stoles. Things you wear around your neck get dirty only in that place where it touches your skin. As the stoles were made of special fabrics that were hard to wash, narrow bands were sewed over these places. They could be taken off and washed or replaced, instead of washing the whole thing.

Bent over my sewing, trying to keep my stitches relatively straight while also trying not to poke myself with the needle, I heard my parents talking about Father Swift.

I knew they liked and respected him so my mother's words did not surprise me.

"He is totally down-to-earth. So loving and caring," Mom said to Dad. "I suspect he grew up quite wealthy, but chose to work in very lowly places."

Dad seemed to be considering this thought. "He is definitely those things, but why do you think he grew up with wealth?"

I saw her grinning mischievously. "He can't iron," she said.

They both laughed.

Later that day, I learned how much my mother also admired the people forced to live in this camp. She was writing a letter to my aunt when Dad came home. He asked if he could read what she was writing.

"Sure," Mom said.

I don't know if Mom expected him to read this out loud, but he did.

"I am in awe of the ability the people here have to keep on going. They have every right to sit down and pout! Instead, they have created a small town community here.

"They have clubs, art classes, baseball and other sports teams, girls' and boys' clubs, preschool—even a newspaper and a library!

"Life goes on as normal, under very abnormal circumstances. There are schools, a clinic, even hairdressers.

"Many of the people incarcerated here were accomplished farmers, and the fields around here are examples of just how good they are at this work. In this hot, flat, dry and windy place, there are acres of lush farmland, producing vegetables, grains and fruits.

"I am so impressed with their work. It really is bone dry here and the dirt hardly seems like productive garden soil. And yet, near their drab, sad barracks are often small gardens of colorful flowers and vegetables. This gives them some extra food, as food is none too plentiful in the mess hall, as well as beauty.

"However, I think what amazes me most is how many people have created so much additional beauty and they can make beauty out of anything.

"Apparently there was scrap lumber around from building the barracks. As these families were only given bed frames and a potbellied stove for warmth, they arrived to find they had nothing, absolutely nothing with which to live! Yet now, many a living quarter has tables, chairs, dressers and cupboards from this lumber.

"I have seen examples, too, of beautiful carvings of wood, also made with this rough scrap. Tiny pieces of jewelry, like pins carved and painted to look like birds, oil and water color paintings, artificial flowers made with shells and ribbons. Traditional dance is taught to the children, and things like masks for these dances are somehow made. It is truly amazing, and, as I said, I am in awe of the creativity as well as the indomitable spirit."

Dad laid the letter on the table. He nodded. "I've seen all this too. I have been amazed ever since we got here, every time I see something like what you describe."

Then my dad, an Irishman at heart, said, "If you tried locking up a couple of Irishmen like this, you'd have non-stop riots!"

He and Mom laughed.

My parents did serious work. I loved it when they stopped to laugh.

It was August now, and hot. So hot.

Mari walked into the house and announced, "I am taking as many kids as I can into town for ice cream and to the wading pool."

Larry was washing dishes. "You can do that?"

I thought of those guards and those guns.

As I said before, Mari, once she had an idea, was like a beach ball in a lake. No matter how hard you try, you can't keep it under water. No one was keeping Mari down!

"I stopped at the administration building. I asked and found out even though the adults aren't allowed to leave the camp without special permission, the kids can go if someone who can leave will take them. But no one ever has. Most of the kids have been here for three years! That means for some of them, they don't even know there is a world outside of these barbed wire fences! But no more! I am taking them to Granada!"

Larry and I both looked at her determined face. "I bet you will," Larry said, with a grin.

A day later, Mari packed our car with kids and then packed some little ones on top of the bigger ones. Larry and I squeezed in too as Mari got behind the wheel.

It was hot and sticky and no one could even wiggle, but Mari called, "Ready?"

We all shouted. "Ready!" And we were off!

Of course, we had to stop at the gate where a guard stood, gun over his shoulder. He slowly approached our big old car, filled to the brim with shouting kids. He slowly opened the gate.

I wondered if any of the little kids might wet their pants in fear. I especially hoped the two on my lap would not. But so far, so good!

Mari, behind the wheel, just gave the guard a smile and called out, "Thanks!"

That prompted all of the kids to yell, "Thanks! Bye!" as that big old car slid out of the prison camp.

"Wave to him," Larry said to the kids on his lap, and so several little arms appeared at the open windows and that guard got more greetings and many a wave.

My sister, brother and I all knew how unwelcoming some of the people in Granada could be. We had felt that the first time we had gone to town. We had also heard stories of "townies" that had welcomed the newcomers. But today, with these excited kids we had come to love, we didn't really think about which reaction we might get.

Mari pulled up to the town wading pool and the car doors flew open. First laughter burst out and then all those kids tumbled out of the car. We ran to the pool, shouting and giggling.

There were mothers already at the pool with their kids. They looked up, startled at the sudden noise. I noticed that their faces changed from surprise to alarm and then to disgust.

The minute our kids got into the pool, one woman got up, went over to the pool and yanked her kids out of the water. The look on her face was nasty.

This caused the other mothers to leave their books and conversations and get their kids out of the pool too.

Some of our kids, especially the little ones, didn't notice. They were too excited just to be in the pool. Others did, and I certainly did. I felt a little frightened.

The town children were steered out of the park by their mothers. While their kids protested loudly that they didn't want to go home yet, the mothers were even louder, making rude remarks about us.

I looked at Larry. He had been swishing Tomomi around in the water, but he looked at me and said, "You'd think we were lepers."

I glanced around at the kids I knew had heard the rude mothers. They either looked hurt or bewildered.

And Mari? She announced, "More room for us!" and began splashing Katherine and Edna.

The rest of us took our cue from her and began playing with abandon.

And oh, how sweet and cool was that ice cream that slid down our throats a couple of hours later! We sat together in a town that didn't want us and enjoyed ourselves immensely!

When we arrived back, a different guard was on duty. He took one look at the car, and of course heard all the kid noise, and opened the gate. He never asked for identification. I suppose he already knew of us from the previous guard.

Though I had two kids on my lap, I was near a window. I was able to look at him from behind Itsuo's wiggles. And I swear there was a smile on that guard's face.

After that, Mari set up many more trips to town for swimming and ice cream.

The excitement on the way there, the joy at the pool, and the giggles over the ice cream never wavered. It was the best ever. Simply the best!

Back in our quarters that first day, I had a lot of fun telling our parents all about the delights of our adventure.

But I thought about the mothers. They had been enjoying themselves before we came. Why had they let the arrival of the camp kids ruin their afternoon? What caused them to ruin not only their time, but their children's play too? I knew all about the prejudice and fear behind this situation, and yet,

I just couldn't understand why a parent would see someone else's kids and act as they did. Who had caused this fear to become so very strong?

The next day, I was again confronted with the feeling of being shunned. We got word, or just sensed attitudes, that some of the staff people did not approve of Mari's excursion with the kids.

These adults seemed to resent her, a 16-year-old girl. They seemed to think she was trying to be a hero or something.

But nothing could have been further from Mari's mind. She didn't want praise. She wanted to give the kids a break from a world that had imprisoned them and took away their childhood.

I wondered if these staff members felt guilty because she was doing something they could have done, but had never chosen to.

But, that beach ball named Mari wasn't bothered at all that some people were irritated by her actions.

She loved the kids, and the kids loved her and tomorrow they'd have more fun!

With Dad's work and our involvement with life in a relocation center, we now had a better understanding of how this imprisonment of innocent people had come about.

Still my parents had more questions and our friend, Father Swift, was the logical one to ask.

He had come over to give Mari another language lesson, and then we all gathered over glasses of cold tea.

"I heard about the field trips to the wading pool and ice cream shop," Father Swift said. The grin on his face showed his delight. "Mrs. Naya said her kids could hardly sleep that first night after they went! And I have heard kids singing songs recently that I think must be handed down from someone's summer camp experience. Could you three have anything to do with that?"

We laughed. Yes, we had taught the kids songs we knew from our summer camp adventures.

I was irritated that Amache was most often called a camp. Real camps had places for evening campfires, lakes with canoes and docks for swimming.

Instead this so-called camp had buildings where people lined up to get food that didn't nourish them.

And there were rows and rows and more rows of low, cramped, shabby barracks where the inmates tried to live as human beings. These were not homes, for this was like a prison, a prison for families, for children, for grandparents. It was for people who had done nothing wrong.

I shook my head a little to come out of this angry daydream and found an intense conversation was going on.

Apparently someone had asked Father Swift about how his order, Maryknoll, had responded after the bombing of Pearl Harbor as they were already working with many Americans of Japanese ancestry.

"Those of us on the West Coast tried to keep life as normal as we could. At the same time, we had to keep our eyes and ears open for information. We were very worried that something like this imprisonment might happen," he said.

"In our schools, we celebrated the Feast of the Immaculate Conception on December 8, and managed to have a wonderful Christmas. Babies were baptized, children made their First Communion as usual."

I smiled at Mom and she winked. On the couch was the sweet little white dress she was making for Mikiko's First Communion.

"But we were also working on ways to act, if necessary. More and more, we were getting convinced that there would be some kind of mass imprisonment. We worked on plans to be able to offer ways for all the families of our schools, or of a church parish, to leave the area the government was labeling unsafe."

Dad whistled. "How could you pull that off?"

"Well, we tried very hard, but the numbers of people were so huge we eventually saw we couldn't get them all moved and settled somewhere else. And time ran out—the government stopped all the people from voluntarily leaving the area so fast after announcing the incarceration. There was no choice for many but to go to the government camps."

"What did you do then?" Mom asked.

"We did what we could do, in a variety of ways. For example, we made certain that children who had Japanese names on their birth certificates also had their certificates of their baptisms to go with them. These showed their Christian names, names that would sound more American to anyone who read them. We thought this might be helpful. We offered places to store people's belongings in our school buildings before they left."

"That may prove to be a big help to those people," Dad said. "I am afraid there are many who will return to find all their things stolen or vandalized. Perhaps at least some people will be spared that."

"So then, the time to leave really arrived. What did you do then?" Mari asked.

"We went to help with the arrival of so many people to these so-called camps. I think about 80 Maryknollers went to a place called Manzanar."

"And you came here, to stay," I said.

He smiled at me. "Yes, there are others from Maryknoll who chose to get into these centers. Some of us actually live in the camps, some of us have to live in nearby towns and travel to the camp each day."

"So are there many priests and sisters in the other centers?" I asked. And I added, because I realized I have never asked this, "How many other centers are there?"

"Oh yes. I think there are 10 centers and there are Maryknollers in at least eight of them. Some sisters, including two who are American-born Japanese who could have stayed in New York, but chose to live in and work in a center. Some of our brothers, and numerous priests—maybe 15 of us."

"Ten centers?" Larry asked.

Father Swift nodded and took a sip of the warming lemonade.

"This is a big place! Lots of land is used. Where did all this land for 10 centers come from?" Mari asked.

Dad said, "I just found out that many of the centers were built on land that were reservations for Native Americans."

Father Swift closed his eyes for a moment, taking in this information. "One wrong after another," he said.

Later I met Katherine and Richard at the little library. While they looked for books, I opened up a thesaurus. I wanted to look up a word that described something I had been thinking about: unfair.

I made a list:

Unfair

Unjust

Dishonest

One-sided

Biased

Prejudicial

Discriminating

Bigoted

Then I looked up "unjust," because that was one of the words I thought described what happened here. I found more words:

Undue

Underserved

Unreasonable

Excessive

Every one of these words described all the wrong I was seeing.

Well, I could do something right today. Something little but right.

"Hey ,Katherine," I whispered. "Can you and Richard come over to my place? Maybe we can have some popcorn."

August 6th seemed like any other summer morning for me.

But for people in a city in Japan, it was the worst, most horrific day ever. And for some 70,000 it was their very last day.

I knew the war was not over yet, even though the Nazis had quit fighting. I knew our country and others were still fighting with Japan.

But I was not thinking about war that morning. Mari, Larry and I were getting ready to take kids to the pool when Dad walked in.

He had left his office to come and tell us that our country had dropped a bomb on Hiroshima, a city in Japan. It was called an "atomic" bomb and it was the most powerful bomb ever.

Dad had heard about this on the radio in the office.

He was extremely upset. He said that the report was the worst thing he had ever heard. "And I think as the day goes on, it will get worse and worse," he said.

Mom looked at us kids. We were in swimming suits.

She said quietly. "Today is not a good day to take the children to town."

Dad glanced up. I don't think he had even noticed us yet.

"No, no," he said hastily. "Not a good idea. But, Mari, you should change clothes and drive into town and buy lots of newspapers. Get as many different ones as you can, but also buy more than one copy of each." He reached into his pocket for his wallet.

"Larry, you go with her."

They both nodded. I have no idea why I wasn't to go. I wasn't sure Dad was concentrating on things like that, so I said nothing.

He handed the money to Mari and said, "We will take them to the library so others can read them too."

There were very few radios on the base, and newspapers were not delivered here.

Despite seeming rattled at this news, Dad was still thinking about others who needed to read this news too.

Mari and Larry returned with piles of newspapers.

President Harry S. Truman made an announcement from a cruiser ship in the Atlantic Ocean. He said this bomb was more than 2,000 times more powerful than any other bomb.

"It is thought that about 60 percent of the city of Hiroshima has been destroyed," Larry read.

Mom looked at some of the photos. She was crying. Then she said, "I have never kept world events from you, but I think it would be best if you avoided looking at these pictures. I can't—I don't—oh, I must go pray," she said, and went into the bedroom.

We didn't think it could get any worse. But then three days later, the United States dropped a second atomic bomb on another Japanese city called Nagasaki.

It was like a recurring nightmare.

"So many more deaths," Mom murmured. "So much more unspeakable suffering."

Dad sat at the table, his head in his hands. I wondered if he was praying or crying. Maybe both. I closed my eyes and prayed.

When I opened them, Dad was saying to Mom, "Americans don't know how to feel about this. Our country has been fighting Japan, and many of our people have died in that fight. And this bombing might be the end of this war ... but was this the way to do it? Was this the only way to end this war? I know, it has gone on and on, and so many people all over the world have been killed, or lost loved ones, or are homeless. But now, thousands and thousands more..."

"I read that some people are scared that Japan could bomb one of our cities now," Larry said.

I thought of saying, "Shut up, Larry!" I had thought of that too and was scared.

But then, Larry was probably scared too. And he was just trying to make sense out of this, as Mom and Dad were.

Even though it was hot out, Mari made some hot tea. She brought a cup to both Mom and Dad. Then she gave one to Larry and me. Then she got herself one and motioned for us to sit down with Dad.

"Let's all pray together," she said.

We did. And then we were silent for a few minutes until Mom said, very gently and very quietly to Dad, "You have important work. Go do it. It will be a form of prayer."

He looked at her. I think if I had taken a picture of him at that moment, the caption would be, "You have a strength that is amazing. What would I do without you?"

Of course, I didn't really know. But it was a look of pure love. That was for sure.

August 15th arrived. That was the feast of the Assumption of Mary, the Mother of God.

Of course there was Mass. Mari had gone early to get the organ and music set up. Dad would go to work later. Going to church on a holy day was as important as going on a Sunday.

Mom, Larry, Dad and I walked towards the barrack/church. From a distance, we saw Father Swift hurrying in.

"I wonder if he will say anything about the bombings," Larry said.

The little church filled up quickly. Though this feast day would have been a celebration, there was a subdued feeling. The past nine days had been horrible for the whole world. Many of the people sitting with us today had lost relatives in Japan. Everyone seemed tired. Even the little kids were not squirmy. Only the babies seemed oblivious to the sad atmosphere.

Father Swift stood, but motioned to Mari and the choir not to sing. He faced all of us. Speaking first in Japanese and then in English, he said, "Japan has surrendered. The war is over."

These were words we had waited so long to hear. But everyone remained silent.

I looked around as politely as I could. The worry and pain etched on the faces of so many of the adults told me that maybe being able to stay silent at the news just because one was in church was a tiny gift to them.

Maybe they didn't know if they wanted to rejoice, slump down in relief, or sob.

So wisely, Father Swift began to pray.

The next time we went to church, it felt a little happier.

Little Mikiko came in with her family. She was dressed in the sweetest little white dress, with embroidered forget-me-nots around the hem and a bit of lace on the collar. On her head she wore a wreath of delicate artificial flowers. They were pink and yellow, colors that stood out beautifully against her jet-black hair. And she was radiant.

She held her mother's hand and they walked up to the front of the room. Her father carried Tomomi and Itsuo walked beside him. They were all as dressed up as anyone could be after three years—Tomomi's whole life—in a prison.

Mari started to play the organ and the choir sang and Father Swift stood smiling at Mikiko.

When it was time for Communion, Mikiko went first, with her parents beside her.

Mari led the choir in singing "Panis Angelicus." That means "Bread of Angels." I knew Mari had chosen this especially for Mikiko today.

It wasn't an easy song to sing and Mari and others had worked hard on it. Mari had also prepared Mikiko for this moment, and for the rest of her life.

And my mom had worked in the background to help make this event more special.

When Mikiko turned around, having just received the Body of Christ for the first time, she was smiling. And I realized she had lost her top two teeth since I had last seen her!

Amache was closing. The war was over. The innocent people who had been imprisoned for over three years were no longer considered dangerous.

This was the first of the camps to close. The last official day would be October 15.

The summer was almost over. On September 2nd, the Japanese formally surrendered. There was a ceremony onboard a U.S. battleship called the USS Missouri in Tokyo Bay. That ship was chosen because President Truman was from Missouri.

He declared this to be V-J Day, meaning "victory over Japan."

We saw newspaper photos of people celebrating, starting on August 15. Some celebrations were solemn and others were raucous and loud. The streets of New York City were so filled with rejoicing people I didn't know they could move! And there was a photograph of a sailor kissing a woman in a white dress. It was to become a very famous picture.

There were also pictures of prisoners of war, men who had spent months in Japanese prisons. They were so thin it was hard to look at them, but they were smiling because the war was over and they could go home.

But at Amache, things were quiet that day. I saw no one celebrating. Most people, I think, were grateful it was over, but now they faced going home.

I say "faced" because it was a time of worry and anxiety for most of them. Was there a home to go to? Was there a job? Would any of their things be still there? Would they and their children be accepted or would they have to deal with still more prejudice?

My dad worked long hours, trying to help. He'd come home late, eat some supper and collapse into bed.

Father Swift came over one day to tell us he would soon be leaving. He needed to get back to the West Coast to help with the resettling of the internees who would return there.

"I have one more favor to ask of you, Mari," he said. "I will be closing down the church here, before many of the people leave. I have made arrangements with the priests in nearby towns. They have agreed to accept any of the people from here if they want to go to Mass."

Mom stared at him. I could tell she was horrified that a priest had to be asked to accept someone who wanted to go to church! Hardly the teachings of Jesus!

But hate and mistrust were rampant these days and he had no idea how a parish might receive these short-term guests. Right now, Father Swift was just tying up loose ends and he went on, "So I am wondering if you would be willing to drive people to the churches."

"Sure," Mari said.

The people in the camps were free to go. Dad helped them get information, get a place to live, or anything else he could do.

We watched the camp folding up around us. The newspaper office, clinic, and library were closed down. There were fewer and fewer people in the mess hall each day.

We were happy or worried for our new friends—or both. And it was a little sad, in a strange sort of way.

We said good-bye to Edna and Mollie. It was clear they would remain life-long friends with Mari, and it was hard to part.

I stood outside as Mikiko's family boarded a truck that would take them to a train, and then to who knows where. I didn't know what arrangements her parents had been able to make.

Tomomi clung to her mother. She was so bewildered. She had never lived anywhere else!

She did not know there could be a neighborhood with trees and no barbed wires and guards with guns.

Mikiko sat between her grandparents, smiling shyly and waving to me.

And Itsuo sat with his father, his eyes shining with excitement.

"Godspeed," I called, knowing they couldn't hear me.

Blinking back tears, I went back into our barracks. It would be a couple of weeks before we would be leaving, as there was more work for Dad to finish up here.

We weren't going back to Chicago yet. Dad had asked to be transferred to another camp that would not be closing as quickly as Amache.

"We are going to Tule Lake, in northern California," Mom had told us. "Dad will be a project attorney, just like he was here."

I wasn't surprised or upset.

PART
❹

❏ ❏ ❏

ON THE WAY TO
TULE LAKE

Tule Lake Segregation Center

A while back, I told you about the long and worldwide war, my dad's work and why we ended up going to the Amache Relocation Center in Colorado. We were amazed at what we found there: a huge prison holding innocent people behind barbed wire fences, with the help of guards with guns.

Now we were heading off to another so-called camp, Tule Lake, in northern California, close to the Oregon border.

I guess we thought we knew what to expect as we had already lived at Amache for about four months: guards, fences, interesting people and bad food. A situation that shouldn't have happened, but there were a few ways we could help make it a little better.

And yes, all those things were there. But this situation was— well, I looked up words in a dictionary to find the right one to describe this so you'd understand. And I found 6 words that fit:

Tule Lake center was:
harsh
infuriating
grievous
distressing
difficult
and agonizing

for the people who were imprisoned there. And remember— these people had not done anything to cause them to be in prison! They were all forced to go there by the government.

As I said earlier, Amache was the first of the 10 centers to close, so my dad volunteered to go to another. Do you know the old expression, "out of the frying pan and into the fire"? It means to go from one bad situation into another that is much worse. Well, that describes us. We left Amache and were tooling along in our big, old 1937 convertible, heading towards a fire of sorts.

So, as long as we were traveling, I decided to tell you about the injustice and confusion that turned Tule Lake Relocation Center into something called a 'segregation center'.

The fastest way to describe the difference is to say that our experience at Tule Lake would make the challenging time at Amache seem almost like a vacation!

You may remember that two years ago, in 1943 when I was 10, we had never heard of the War Relocation Authority, or WRA. But that does not mean it wasn't busy. It had already imprisoned something like 120,000 innocent people. So by 1943, the WRA was beginning to think there might be legal problems as a result!

So they came up with some questions for all adults who were Japanese and Japanese-American. These were on a form that was named something like "Application for Leave Clearance," but quickly got called the "loyalty questionnaire." It was supposed to help the government figure out who would be loyal and who would be disloyal to the United States.

They wanted to know this for two main reasons:

They were looking for young Japanese-American men who would join the army to fight in the war.

The WRA was also trying to figure out who they would let out of the prisons and who they would keep in.

But two of the questions were really confusing, and this would lead to terrible problems for thousands of people. To quote my mother, even the wisest man in ancient history, King Solomon, would have struggled to solve the issues these questions caused.

The really crazy thing is that these questions could only be answered with either a "yes" or a "no." But the questions were written in a way that was just not clear.

One person might read a question and think it meant one thing, and her neighbor might read it and think it meant something else!

Two brothers who agreed on what the question meant might be confused how to answer it. Even though they wanted to give the same information, one thought "yes" expressed that, while the other said "no" answered it.

Some people were so confused they decided not to answer at all. But the government counted any unanswered question as "no."

This was a big deal because what you answered affected what would happen to you when the war was over!

The government made lists of people according to their answers. Some people were put on a list that claimed they were loyal to the United States. Others were put on a list that labeled them as disloyal.

So you can imagine that these unclear questions caused tons and tons of problems. They also caused people who were already in prison to have more fear, more sadness, and more anger.

And now, with their lists of "loyal" and "disloyal" people, the WRA decided they needed a place to put all these "disloyal" people.

Again, remember these people had done nothing wrong! And now, because they thought the best answer to an unclear question was "no," they had become "problem" people.

The government's solution to this ridiculous issue was to take one of the 10 relocations centers and turn it into a "segregation center."

The word "segregate" has two meanings:

To separate or set apart from others or from the general group; for example, you could segregate all the cherry-flavored jellybeans from the other flavors.

To cause or force the separation of something or someone; an example is what happened after the bombing of Pearl Harbor when one group, the Japanese-Americans, were forced to live apart from other people.

So to segregate these so-called disloyal people, the WRA changed Tule Lake Relocation Center into a segregation center.

And this is how you do that:

You try to get the "loyal" prisoners to move to a different center. At Tule Lake about 6,000 people left for other centers. But many others said, "You have already forced us to leave our homes! The war is almost over. We are tired and discouraged. We are going to stay here until you say we can go home!" So some left, but there were still 4,000 there. Still, you start bringing in all the "disloyal people" anyway. Pretty quickly, things get really crowded.

You make the barbed wire fences around the prison more secure: you make them even higher and you add another fence, so you have a really high, double fence.

You add more guard towers. There were six already—six towers with armed guards with guns peering down on kids on their way to school, or adults going to their work. Now you have more built so there are 28! Twenty-eight!

And you bring in 1,000 more soldiers to be guards. One thousand soldiers!!!! (which makes an already overcrowded place 1,000 people more crowded!)

And in case that wasn't enough, you bring in 6 big, scary army tanks and park them around, just to let people know they are in an army prison. And maybe drive them around the barracks, which scares people. Terrifies them.

And machine guns. Lots of machine guns.

So, you can see that this place was going to be even more frightening and difficult than Amache was. Can you start imagining how horrible Tule Lake would be?

I can imagine it now, but as I sat in the back seat of the old car, singing with my sister, playing word games with my brother and laughing with my family, I had no idea of any of this.

Nor did I have any idea of how this space would "feel." But you need to know. Again I decided to make a list of some words to describe how people might feel in that place:

tense
anxious
miserable
edgy
worried
jumpy
down-hearted
panicky
upset
depressed
vexed
fearful
desolate

And this is why:
- You take people who have done nothing wrong, and force them to leave everything–their homes, their lands, their jobs, their schools, and their friends. This includes babies, those just born and some unborn, old people, sick people, little kids, teenagers, people with handicaps.
- You move all these people to a very uncomfortable place with bad food and not enough bathrooms. After a couple of years of this, you force them to answer some questions which makes them seem "disloyal" and tell them they must move to another camp.
- 18,000 people, labeled as "disloyal," were sent to Tule Lake, where soldiers, guns, and tanks waited for them.

That would make me jumpy, depressed, vexed and fearful!

But there were even more reasons that this place was so tense:

Many of the people in the camps had been farmers before the war. Now they worked the farm at Tule Lake. There was an accident with a truck carrying them to the fields in which they grew food. Five workers were hurt and one worker died.

- Soon they learned several things that made this even worse: the person driving the truck was not old enough to have been given that job, the family of the man who died would get very little money to live on, and the workers were supposed to ask permission to have a funeral for their friend. Of course these things got people upset!

There were already huge problems. The camp was so overcrowded that the water source had run out of water. And, the sewers no longer worked.

Think about those two things for a minute.

It had become a very unhealthy, filthy, unsafe place.

The farm workers talked and agreed they would stop doing their jobs until they could work out some of these problems. They went on strike.

They asked the camp director to meet with them so the many problems could be discussed. Instead they were all fired!

And, prisoners from other relocation centers were brought in to do the work and get paid. And, they got paid much more money!

All this was way too much. Still, there were only a few fights among frustrated people.

When they learned the director of the WRA was coming, a group was formed to have a meeting with him. Others gathered outside to show that they too hoped there could be some changes to help with the problems. Eventually, about 5,000 people arrived—there were a lot of people in that center! This was a peaceful gathering. I think you might call this an "act of civil disobedience," but I don't think they were even breaking any unfair rules.

But the huge number scared the non-Japanese people running the place.

Martial law was declared. That is when soldiers become the police officers and those in charge can make extra rules.

Now there were rules that said when you could and couldn't be outside.

Activities people enjoyed, like art classes or scout meetings, were shut down.

Even most of the jobs in the camp were ended! This meant families with those jobs had no way of making money!

And lots of people now had nothing to do.

But that was not all.

At any time, soldiers could come into your barracks with guns and search through your things. Picture little kids trying to hide behind their grandpa when suddenly there are soldiers stomping into their small rooms.

Even worse than all these things were shortages of milk, food, hot water and fuel to heat their barracks and plugged sewers.

Instead of solving these problems, those in charge decided to build a prison inside of the prison camp. It was called the stockade.

Those who protested these conditions could be jailed in it. The stockade was much too small for the large number of people they put into it, and some of the people were kept there for many months. They were treated badly and some were even hurt by soldiers. A fence around it was covered with boards so families could not talk to their loved ones in the jail.

And none of these prisoners were given trials.

Nine weeks later, martial law was lifted. That helped, but only a little.

Not all of the people in the "inside-the-prison" prison were allowed to return to their families. And these families were discouraged and confused for many reasons:

Now their sons were being told they must join the army and fight in the war. If they agreed, these young men could be seriously hurt or even killed fighting for the country that had unfairly imprisoned the whole family. If they refused, they could be put into the prison-inside-the-prison for a long time.

In the summer of 1944, President Roosevelt had signed a law saying U.S. citizens could give up their citizenships if they wanted to. That made some people question if they would ever feel accepted and valued in the place of their birth.

Some of the internees were now feeling they should go live in Japan. And they wanted others to go too. They got quite pushy about this. Some children were a little frightened of the people who wanted to go to Japan.

There were fears that even when the war was over, many Japanese-Americans would be treated badly by other Americans. What might happen if they went back to their home towns?

While the WRA said it would close all the relocation camps in the next year, what would happen for those in Tule Lake, the segregation center, was not clear.

Most of the families had people who had come to the United States from Japan years earlier. They were not allowed to ever become citizens, no matter how long they had lived here. But their kids and grandkids were citizens of the United States. Many of them had never even been to Japan. But the elders thought they would have to go to Japan and wanted their families to come with them. And that caused a lot of unhappy discussions and decisions.

After so much time imprisoned in such bad living conditions and so many fears about their future, it was no wonder they were disheartened and confused! Many in the camp decided to give up their citizenship and move to Japan.

Then some had second thoughts. They were worried and frightened, realizing they should have kept their citizenship.

It was a mess.

That is what was going on at Tule Lake by November of 1945.

So as the Hannan family drove along, through Colorado, Utah and Nevada, heading toward California, I wondered what Tule Lake would be like.

I imagined a lot of things, but nothing like what it would really be.

PART
❺

❑ ❑ ❑

FROM RELOCATION TO
SEGREGATION

Tule Lake Segregation Center

I t was November 1945. We had left behind the plains of southeastern Colorado days ago. The scenery had changed several times and so had the temperature. The top was back up on the convertible and the windows were closed.

"I estimate we should arrive in about an hour," Dad said. "I have a little information about the area the center is built on. It will be an interesting place." He handed Larry a piece of paper.

Larry began to read aloud, "Tule Lake Center sits on a dry lakebed, west of some lava beds. For hundreds of years, native peoples, some called the Modoc, lived in the general area according to the seasons. The area around Tule Lake was abundant in water, edible and medicinal plants, waterfowl and other game. In 1826, conflicts with newcomers began. During the Modoc War of 1872-73, many of the Modoc people were forced off the land. They are still struggling today because of that war."

"Lava beds! That must mean that some of the area was formed when a volcano erupted long ago!" I exclaimed and peered out the car window. I had seen photos of lava spewing from a volcano. Now I imagined hot lava surging further and further from a volcano, covering ground and plants, and changing them forever.

Mari had been thinking of a different aspect of this place.

"So this land has seen a people living on it for generations and then forced to leave, and now it is a place where another group of people are forced to stay," she said quietly.

Mom agreed with both of us. "It seems as if this is a place of turmoil, both for the land and people."

Soon we began to see the most recent turmoil.

Our first sight of Tule Lake Segregation Center was of wintering farm fields, and then double, eight foot high, barbed wire fences. There were guard towers on every corner within the fence and more soldiers than I had ever seen in one place.

Pulling up to the gate, Dad said to us, "Welcome to the biggest of the WRA centers. A few months ago there were more than 18,000 people here."

It had been surprising to us how many businesses had been at Amache, so Mari and I began assessing the shops.

"A shoe repair place and a beauty shop," I said.

"A fish shop and funeral parlor," said Mari." And a tofu factory!"

"What's tofu?" asked Larry.

We didn't know so we ignored him. "I see at least a couple of churches, and there is a Buddhist church—'church' may not be the correct word, though."

"I saw a sign for sumo wrestling," I said. "What does 'sumo' mean?"

They didn't know so they ignored me.

"There is a fire station,' Mari said. "And maybe that is a school over there."

Later we would learn that there were also several co-op stores, four judo halls, and a hospital. In all, there were eight Buddhist houses of worship, three Christian churches and three fire stations.

We would later learn that there was an outdoor stage and baseball fields. Farther out, there was a cemetery and the farm fields, which included a hog farm. This was a whole city!

And it was all here because of racial prejudice and fear.

The first morning, I woke up very early because I heard many voices.

I stood on my bed to peer out the window. A large number of young men, all wearing white headbands, were moving past. Most wore white shirts. They were running together, like a high school track team might do before the track season starts.

Then I went to help make breakfast.

"Given that five of the relocation camps have closed since Amache did, and three others may close by the end of this month, I need to get into the work here right away," Dad said, putting brown sugar on his oatmeal.

By now we had learned where the original 10 centers were located

"Which ones will likely close yet this month?" Mari asked.

"Poston in Arizona, Manzanar in California and Rohwer in Arkansas," Dad said.

"Do you know what the plans are for here, at Tule Lake?" Mom asked.

"No, but I think the situation might be very different."

After Dad left, Mom informed us that there was a school within the boundaries of the camp, and a high school in the nearby town of Tulelake. Before the day was done, we kids were enrolled.

I went to the school within the camp. It was a surprising place. Though it had been finished less than two years before, it housed an auditorium/gym, a shop, a science and crafts building, a library and an administration building!

I quickly learned, however that there was a strange divide in the day: many of the students attended classes taught in Japanese in the morning and then classes taught in English in the afternoon.

That day Mom heard the administration was looking for people to work in a lot of different ways. By the following day, she had a job at the camp hospital as a secretary to a medical social worker.

The Hannan family had settled in!

Our barracks was rather chilly, so for dinner that evening we ate potato soup. Mom made that to warm us up as well as fill us up.

I shivered and wondered if the barracks for the Japanese families were as poorly built as the ones at Amache.

"My secretarial skills are pretty rusty," Mom said as she ladled the soup into bowls. "But the hospital has a medical social worker who really needs help. There are people in the hospital who are chronically ill—they have ongoing problems and are so sick their families can't care for them completely. They will need extra help and many will need a place, like a nursing home, to go when the camp closes. I am learning how to make arrangements for them."

I glanced at Dad. He was listening to Mom, but I saw more than that in his face. I wondered what he was experiencing at work.

Mom sat down then, and we said our meal prayer together.

"Bless us, oh Lord, and these thy gifts, which we are about to receive through thy bounty, through Christ, our Lord. Amen."

I took a sip of milk and Mom went on telling us about her day.

"I am learning a great deal about the lives of the people here, even before they were evacuated to relocation centers.

"It is heartbreaking to hear what they have lost– homes, jobs, neighborhoods. Things they treasured that were handed down from grandparents, toys children loved so much, and their pets," she said.

I thought of my dollhouse again.

"And they are so sick and so very tired of being pushed around."

We were silent, partially because we didn't know what to say, and partially, I admit, because we were hungry. The soup in our bowls was disappearing quickly.

She turned to my father. "Did you know that many of the older people, those who immigrated here years ago from Japan, were told when all this happened that they would have to return to Japan when the war was over?"

I heard Dad take in a deep breath. He put down his spoon and said, "The people here are really in serious trouble, Nelle.

Much more than we saw at Amache."

Larry reached for the bread. "Why?"

"Well, it seems that those in power, those who caused all this, are now telling these same people they must take an oath of loyalty to the United States."

I piped up. "Being loyal means to always stick with someone or something, like a school. Like I am loyal to my friends, sticking with them, helping them, things like that. And an oath is a promise, right?"

Mom nodded and added, "A very serious and important promise."

"What about this loyalty oath?" Mari asked, passing the butter to Larry.

My dad had patiently waited for all this to be said. He and Mom always made sure us kids knew what was going on, which often meant a lot of questions and discussion. And he got in a few mouthfuls of soup. But now he put down his spoon a second time and began to explain.

"A couple of years ago, two parts of our government, the War Department and the WRA, were working together and decided they needed a way to figure out which of the people jailed in the centers were loyal to the United States and which ones weren't. They came up with a form for all the internees to fill out if they were 17 or older. How you answered these questions would decide if you were considered loyal or disloyal."

Dad paused and looked at us. I think he was trying to see if we really wanted him to go on. We all just looked back at him and stayed silent. So he took that as a green light.

"For many people, it wasn't too hard to answer. But for others, there were problems. For people who were born in Japan for example. There is a whole generation of people who came here and have lived here for years. But there is a law that says no Japanese people who come to live in the United States can ever become citizens—"

"Most other people immigrating from other countries can become citizens!" Mari exclaimed.

"Like our relatives from Ireland," Larry said.

"Did this law start because of the bombing of Pearl Harbor?" I asked.

Dad smiled at me. I knew he was impressed with my question. That felt very good!

"No Asian people have been allowed to become U.S. citizens since this country began," Dad said.

"That's crazy," Larry said.

I asked, "But their kids who were born in the United States, are citizens, right?"

"That's right, but that wasn't enough to keep them from being put into these centers," Mom said.

Dad looked at each of us then. He must have decided to change to a more cheerful subject.

"More soup, please! You make the best potato soup, Nelle!" he said. "And how was school today?"

Despite Dad's topic change, I thought about this loyalty oath. I had a feeling we would be hearing a lot more about it. It would become a bigger and bigger problem each day in our time at Tule Lake.

I made my first friend there when I met Alice. We were in the same grade at the school. I mentioned to my father that I wanted to invite her over for some after-school popcorn soon.

"I am glad you have a friend here already," Dad said. Then he added, "I think you and Alice will have to go to a guard house to sign something saying she is coming to our house."

"Who must sign?" Mom asked. "Alice's parents or me?"

"I think Helen can sign for Alice," Dad said.

"What?" Mari said. "Alice can't come to our barracks on her own, but another child can sign something so she can? That is crazy—and insulting to Alice!"

I stood there. Suddenly my simple idea to invite Alice over for some popcorn had become a lot to think about.

Dad answered, "Of course it is ridiculous. This whole thing of imprisoning innocent people is ridiculous and this is just another example of the injustice the people here live with every day."

At school, I told Alice about having to sign for her. She nodded. She had been here four years now. Nothing surprised her.

But at the guardhouse, a tall, silent soldier stood over us with a gun in hand. I know we were feeling the same way then: uncomfortable and a little scared. When I picked up the pen to sign the paper, though, the words "ridiculous" and "injustice" came to me. I signed angrily. When I looked up, I saw Alice looking down towards the floor. Was she embarrassed?

I made certain we had a lot of laughs at our barracks. And I made plenty of popcorn.

Sunday morning, we set out to find the Catholic church, which was just another barracks. Not certain where it was in this large place, we had left our quarters early, and as we found it easily, we were early for Mass.

Like at Amache, a Maryknoll priest had been pastoring at Tule Lake. Father Joseph Hunt was outside this cold morning, surrounded by a group of little kids. They were noisy and excited, bumping into each other, stepping on each other's toes. But no one complained. It seemed the priest was handing each of them something, but we could not see what it was.

A couple of kids, happy with whatever it was they had gotten, moved away from the group, saying, "Arigatou Gozaimasu!"

I looked at Mari who said, "It is one way to say 'thank you.'"

We watched as these two boys reached into their coat pockets and pulled out tops for spinning.

"String!" Larry said. "The priest is giving out string to all these kids for their tops!"

Within a few seconds, many children were crouching down and all sorts of homemade tops were spinning on the ground, thanks to the string that Father Hunt was handing out.

A man approached us and introduced himself as Alice's father. He was coming for Mass and had noticed us watching. First he smiled at me and said he had heard about me from Alice and had guessed we were "Helen's family."

Then he nodded toward Father Hunt and the excited kids. Quietly he explained, "He must collect string all the time and everywhere he can get it, because this happens almost every week!"

Both of my parents laughed. "Great idea," Mom said.

"Yes it is," Alice's father agreed. "Many of the children that come each Sunday are not Catholic or of any other Christian religion. Some are Buddhists; some do not have a religion. But all are children who need string and Father Hunt makes certain they get it!"

I saw my mother glancing at Father Hunt and I did too. It was a cold morning and he was wearing a coat. It was the worst coat I had ever seen—no buttons left, but it was so worn, I wasn't certain there were even buttonholes anymore. When he turned to go into church, I saw that one of the side seams was completely ripped open.

No one was dressed in new clothes. The years of war and being imprisoned had caused everyone to look rather shabby, but that coat! I was not certain that, cut into small pieces, it would even make good rags!

A few days later, I was invited to go to Alice's barracks after school.

She did not have to sign anything for me to go to her barracks. Apparently I was free to come and go as I pleased. I think both of us were glad we did not have to go sign anything, but I still felt weird being the privileged one.

As we buttoned up our jackets and pulled caps over our ears, Alice said, "You can see what my obaa-san is making."

I was pretty sure that was a word meaning "grandmother."

We shivered on our way over there and it didn't feel much warmer inside her barracks. Her grandmother was there, a small woman bundled in several layers of sweaters. She was hunched over something she was working on at the homemade table. She looked up at us and smiled.

Alice said something in Japanese. Then to me, she said, "I told her I think you will like what she was making."

She was right.

On the table were several small brooches, a kind of jewelry worn on a coat or sweater and fastened with a pin. They were flowers all made of shells.

One looked like a peony in full bloom, with its rows of tiny white shells placed in circles that got smaller and smaller.

There was another made of very pale pink shells, and was as beautiful a rose as I had ever seen.

I was afraid to touch them, as they looked so delicate. I think I sighed my amazement because Alice's grandmother smiled.

"This is my favorite," Alice said, pushing a pin towards me. I caught my breath. It was so beautiful!

"Lily of the valley!" I said. "And wild roses!" I couldn't take my eyes off that pin.

Her grandmother looked questionably at Alice so she translated my words into Japanese. Her grandmother lit up as she understood. She looked into my eyes with a tenderness that brought a lump to my throat. She said something I couldn't understand.

Alice said quietly, "She is impressed. She said you know your flowers well."

Suddenly, the memory of my Grandpa came rushing through me.

"My grandfather was a good gardener. He loved flowers too," I said.

Alice didn't need to translate. Her grandmother took my hand into both hers and held it. We were silent.

Over a bowl of hot cereal the next morning, I asked, "Does anyone know who these men are who run past here every morning? They wear white headbands and they shout a lot."

"I think there are groups of people who are planning on going to Japan when they leave here. Some are learning to speak Japanese, or trying to get better at it. Some are exercising so they are in good health for the trip," Mari said.

Dad was pulling on his coat. "It is more than that. There is a large number of people here at Tule Lake who have become very pro-Japan. Many young men are angry at the way they have been treated by the American government—first, taken from their homes and schools and put into these prisons, and then a couple of years ago, there comes this questionnaire I mentioned. It asks if they are loyal to the US, but also asks if they will join the army. Some feel, 'why should we join the army when our government has imprisoned us for no reason, even though we are citizens?' They are angry and there has been a lot of protesting here at Tule Lake. Some have formed a group called the Hoshi Dan, and it is a militant group."

"And this Hoshi Dan group is made up of the men who go running and exercising?" I asked.

"Yes, but there are other members too. Many have been thrown into jail for trying to get the rights they should have as citizens," Dad said. "By jail, I mean the stockade here within this prison's grounds. And now I really must leave for work."

Larry was stacking the cereal bowls into the sink but he looked at Dad. "Some of the Hoshi Dan are pressuring the younger boys, ones my age. Some of these kids are from families who don't want them to take part in any protesting."

Dad stopped and looked at Larry.

"I think they are scared, Dad," Larry said quietly.

"There is a lot for them to be worried about," Dad said.

They stood there for a moment, their eyes exchanging something very important. Father and son.

On Thursday, Alice and I pulled on our warmest mittens and caps because we were off on an adventure! We were shell hunting.

Bored and frustrated, many of the people who lived at the Tule Lake center had looked for ways to be creative. At first they had few materials to work with. But then kids who played in the very sandy areas came back with lots of shells, and things got better for the artistic people. Adults began digging and sifting sand too. They discovered that there were layers of shells–in fact, whole veins of shells.

I followed Alice over the lava rocks to the sandy areas. I tried to ignore the guard tower. I was determined Alice and I were going to have fun.

"You saw the brooches my obaa-san makes," Alice said. "She also made my mother a lovely necklace with some of the tiniest shells. It is a soft white, and so delicate!

"Lots of people here make things with shells," she went on. "I saw the most beautiful box made by my mother's friend— the whole outside was covered with different-sized shells! Of course, you have to really dig to find so many. And you also have to dig to find the different kinds of shells. Sometimes someone finds a vein of shells and digs four feet down!"

I laughed and held up my small hand shovel. "I don't expect we will go that far!"

As I looked around for shells, I thought about how bored I would get if I had lived here as long as Alice had. Did making things really help?

Lost in that thought, I said suddenly, "I saw lots of beautiful paintings and carvings when I was at Amache."

She was sitting on the cold sand, digging, and didn't look up. "Yes, people find making things helpful in many ways," she said. "When they first came here, they made furniture from scrap lumber. You can't live in a place and only have beds! And then as kids outgrew their clothes and the weather became colder, grown-ups began making clothes and sweaters and blankets—other things we needed. But we also make things that are just for being beautiful. Obaa-saan says that people need to live with beauty to feel happy. And they need to make beauty to be healthy."

Suddenly, Alice's shovel unearthed several shells. She gave a little excited cry. I scooted over to her and we began digging together. She sifted through the sand with cold fingers and found more. I shook sand off them and carefully set them into the cloth bag we had brought.

We kept on digging, sifting, discovering shells and talking.

It was a wonderful afternoon.

"Helen," Mom said. "Father Hunt told me he takes kids on little outings, to get them out of the camp sometimes. Would you like to go with them this weekend?"

Of course I wanted to go!

Two days later, clad in a winter coat and rubber boots, I ran through the snow to meet Father Hunt and the other kids. I squeezed into a car with Alice, her friend Tomiko, and several other kids.

We laughed and sang and had a great time on the way. Still, I kept looking out the window, for I was seeing a landscape totally new to me. When we arrived, we ran, jumping over snow-covered rocks, until we came to open water. It was definitely cold enough that any ponds should have been ice-covered.

Instead, the water was bubbly and warm! This was the end of November, but this water was actually warm! I knew it was because it was steamy and because all the other kids had jumped in—and stayed in!

Of course I joined them. I stepped into the water with my knee-high boots protecting my feet, but I could still feel the warmth of the water.

The others were laughing and splashing and shouting. I remembered that these kids only got to leave the camp every once in a while. I had arrived just a few weeks ago. No matter what they were doing, they would have been excited. I played too, but every once in a while, I had to stop and take it all in.

Rocks and snow surrounded the little pool of wonderfully warm water we played in. Snow and hot water—I still couldn't get over that!

Then I noticed something just on the edge of the water. It was green and growing! I waded over to it. It was watercress, a wonderful herb that tasted just a bit spicy.

I picked a little and nibbled it. As I savored that green and zesty taste, I thought about it being November, and that I had walked through snow and gotten into warm water and then picked fresh leaves of watercress.

Now that is not something you get to do every day!

After all the splashing and laughter, we trudged back to the car. The sun was going down as we all piled into the car. Father Hunt handed out some snacks he had brought and we headed back to the center.

One of the kids said that he wished we didn't have to go back.

Well, he sort of got his wish, because halfway back, the car broke down. It slowed, made chugging sounds and did a few jerks, then little by little came to a halt.

Father Hunt hopped out and popped open the hood. With it up, we couldn't see him, but when he got back into the car, it was pretty obvious by his face that we weren't going anywhere for a while. I don't know if he didn't know how to fix it or realized he couldn't fix it on the side of the road.

We all watched for another car to come along. We didn't expect many, as this was a remote area. After about a half hour someone came along, and Father Hunt was out of the car in an instant, waving it down.

He had a quick conversation with the driver, and the car sped off. Father Hunt got back into the car and said the driver had agreed to send help.

But it got dark, and no one had come.

We kids huddled in the car to keep warm. At first it was fun. We told stories and sang songs. I talked a lot with Tomiko and realized I now had a second friend at Tule Lake.

A couple of hours passed and we were getting hungry and restless. Still no help came. I think Father Hunt was afraid to leave us and go look for help. And he wasn't going to send any of us out at night and in the cold.

Alice and the littler kids fell asleep. Tomiko and I talked for a while longer, but then she too fell asleep.

It was very dark, as there were no streetlights. I gazed out the window at the stars overhead. The night sky seemed so huge. Vast, I think is a better word for it.

Everything was quiet. I thought about my mother's belief that guardian angels watch over us.If I were ever going to see one, this place of wild beauty would be perfect.

I felt quite safe, so maybe the angels were there!

I noticed Father Hunt checking his watch. It must have been close to midnight! I guess I started to doze too but startled awake when I heard the car door being opened and shut very quietly.

Of course I opened my eyes.

Father Hunt was just outside of the car now. He had turned the car lights on. Maybe he must have done this because anyone driving along might not even notice our dark car. Probably he was assuming someone from the camp would be looking for us by now.

Perhaps that is why he had turned on the car lights, but I soon realized he had a different plan too. He was holding his Breviary prayer book.

He went around to the front of the car and sat down on the bumper.

Curious, I sat up more. I could see the side of his face and realized he was holding his prayer book in the glow of one of the headlights.

Probably with all the activity of the day, and then the concerns about the car and the kids, Father had just remembered that he hadn't finished reading his Breviary, the special prayers a priest says every day.

He was ordained first and foremost as God's priest, and he was not forgetting that. If he found himself stranded with a broken car and bunch of sleepy kids in the middle of winter, he would take care of everything as well as he could. But he would not neglect his prayers, either.

I shivered and wondered how cold it must be, sitting out there, wearing that threadbare coat of his. But I understood that despite the cold and the late hour, despite the fact that he was probably worried about us kids, he seemed focused on his prayers. There was a sense of peace about him.

I fell asleep then. Sometime after midnight, someone from the center must have figured out where we were, because when I woke up it was because of the glare from the searchlights at the gates of the center.

I stumbled into my bed a little while later and said sleepily to my mother, "I will never forget this day."

It was snowing as Tomiko and I hurried from the guardhouse. Once again, I signed under the gaze of a silent soldier holding a gun and wondered how Tomi felt about this rule.

We were going to study together at my quarters. There was a big geography test the next day. As we walked, she asked me about my family.

"I am the youngest," I said. "Larry is two years older than me, and Mari is four years older. Mari is courageous and will do all sorts of gutsy things if it means helping someone. Larry is quieter, but he is always asking questions. He gets angry when he sees things that are wrong and nobody is doing things about it."

Tomi giggled a little at my description. Snowflakes settled onto her black hair, like tiny jewels.

"I'm also the third child, but I am not the youngest—I have a little brother too. The two older than me are also brothers," Tomi said as we hurried along.

"Yosh is in the army. We think he is in Italy. He is in the 442nd Regimental Combat Team. All the soldiers are Japanese-Americans. They are getting famous for how brave they are."

I listened. I didn't know much about this unique unit.

"They have more medals and awards than any other in the army!" Tomi said proudly. "Of course we worry about Yosh a lot, too."

"And your other older brother?"

"Yes, Jiro. He is a just a year younger than Yosh. He's here with us. Do you know about the questionnaire that everyone has to fill out? The one asking about loyalty?"

I nodded. My nose was getting cold and I was anxious to reach our quarters.

But Tomiko seemed lost in her thoughts. "Jiro has been going through agonies trying to decide whether or not to sign the loyalty oath. He is loyal and loves this country, but he is very angry about what is happening to our family."

I started to say we were almost to my barracks but she was so focused on her concerns, she went on, "He talks about how they have locked up our obaa-san and our baby brother. And me, his little sister. We are in this prison for no reason that makes any sense.

"Jiro says he has 'to make a statement against this evil injustice and all the harm it has caused,'" she said. "I know he respects what Yosh has chosen to do, but Jiro feels really strongly about this. Helen, I am worried about him too, in a different way."

We ran up the steps and into the warmth of our barracks. With some hot chocolate Mari had made for us, we settled down to study.

The names of the countries in Europe were on the test. The teacher had given us a blank map for us to fill out.

"Italy," Tomi said, writing that in the correct space on her map.

"The one that looks like a boot," I said.

"The one where Yosh is," she said, wistfully.

I tried to concentrate on my map but kept thinking how crazy it was that Tomi could name all those countries but couldn't go beyond the fence here.

And what was even crazier was that her brother was in one of them, fighting for the country that was keeping his family in prison.

❧

It was snowing quite heavily again when Father Hunt arrived. Dad had invited him over for dinner.

Soon we were around the table, exchanging stories of where our lives had taken us. We had just learned that Father Hunt had worked in Korea for several years. That was where he was when Pearl Harbor was bombed.

"I knew I had to get back to the United States as soon as possible then," he said.

"I managed to get to Japan. There I was able to get aboard the Gripsholm. That ship is actually a Swedish ocean liner, but right now it is being used by the United States for moving people around because of the war—bringing Japanese citizens back to Japan and U.S. and Canadian citizens back here."

"What was it like to be in the middle of the ocean during a world war?" Mom asked.

"The Gripsholm is considered a neutral ship and so it was lit up at night– bright, white lights. Of course, all other ships were blacked out, and when they came anywhere near us, our lights revealed them. They hurried away from us as quickly as possible," he said.

Larry gave a low whistle. "I bet that was sort of strange for everyone! In the middle of all that water, in all that darkness, and then one lit-up ship! "

I closed my eyes, trying to imagine the feel of being on a ship and what it would be like to be in the middle of the ocean. And what it might be like to be in the only light for hundreds of miles.

I came back from my imaginary ocean trip to hear Larry say, "When you could suddenly see another ship nearby, did you wonder if it was someone you could trust?"

"Well, I was on a big ship so it could never have gotten really close to other ships, of course," said Father Hunt. "It was not possible to see anyone on the other ships. But yes, there was some fear whenever we got closer to another ship, even though we were clearly neutral."

Dad asked him about his time here at Tule Lake. They talked for a while, and then Father Hunt turned to Mari.

"I hear you might be willing to do some shopping," he said.

Dad smiled and I knew immediately how Father Hunt had heard that Mari was always looking for a challenge.

"Sure," Mari said.

"I do most of the shopping in the town called Tulelake. It is a pretty big job," Father Hunt said, looking first toward our parents and then at Mari again.

Larry and I grinned at each other. We both knew Mari would never pass up a chance to make things better. She was kind of fierce that way.

"I imagine it is. I can do that," she said confidently.

As Mom and Dad seemed to agree, Father Hunt began explaining more.

"The adults can't leave camp, of course, so most shopping has to be done by catalog. That process takes a long time, sometimes weeks, and usually those companies don't want you to send cash, which is all the people here have. There are the co-op stores here, but they can't carry much. You can't buy so much as a toothbrush here. I would be really grateful if you could do this shopping, Mari."

"So you have done all this shopping until now?" Dad asked him. "Only you?"

"Yes, on Saturdays I head to Tulelake with my shopping list," Father Hunt said.

"Your only day off," Mom noted.

He shrugged and explained away his generosity with his time. "The people have been imprisoned for so long, they need things for their families. And, of course, they are hoping they will soon be leaving, so they may need some other things for when they travel.

"The list can get long, and people need quite a variety of things. Actually, there are some things that may be easier for you to buy than me. Like lipstick."

We all chuckled, thinking of him in a store, choosing lipstick colors. But this also helped us think about what a big deal it had been for him.

"One time I had to buy a suit for a man. That was hard in a different way, trying to guess the best size for someone who is not with you! And of course, there are the lemon drops."

"Lemon drops?" I asked.

He smiled. "Yes. Mrs. Ikejeri likes to have a supply on hand for her grandchildren!"

We laughed a little again, and Mom passed the mashed potatoes around.

"You may not find this shopping easy. Not all the shopkeepers in Tulelake are happy to be selling things to people who are Japanese. This segregation center does not have a good reputation in town.

"Why not?" I asked.

"Well, Helen, it seems that a lot of false stories were spread," he said. "For a while, townspeople actually believed that the people here were enjoying steaks, ham and roasts! Of course, the townspeople, like most of us, were having to deal with food shortages and rationing because of the war, so if they thought there was great food in the camp, they would get pretty angry."

Larry made a face as if he was going to bite someone. "I could tell them how crazy that idea is! We are so lucky we can cook in our quarters, but the people forced to live here have awful food—and never enough!" Larry said.

"I imagine some of the conflicts here in the center were also viewed badly," Dad said.

Father Hunt nodded. "Yes, there have been issues here. When those happened, newspaper articles were published that made it seem much worse than anything that really happened. Of course, that caused the local people to become frightened of what they assumed were dangerous Japanese POWs, that is prisoners of war, in their midst," he explained.

"It was so frustrating. If the townspeople could only understand what the issues are. Workers went on strike because salaries were incredibly low and some of the work was unsafe.

"And some of the unrest was over huge problems of the basic needs —the water ran out at one point, for heaven's sake! And the sewers stopped working! It was terrible.

"People were truly suffering! But when the townspeople heard about protests, they never asked if it was about human dignity or civil rights. They jumped to the conclusion it was a threat by those disloyal to the country."

Once again, he looked at Mari. "So, having heard all this, do you still want to do the shopping?"

"Yes," she said immediately.

"She can do this." I said. "Mari is like Saint Joan of Arc."

Saturday morning dawned cold and dry. It would be a good day to drive to Tulelake and do the camp shopping.

Father Hunt had gotten the shopping list and money together for Mari. "When they pick up their things you buy today, they will meet you. So then after that they can find you and give you their lists and money for the week," he said. "Again, Mari, I can't tell you how much I appreciate you doing this shopping!"

Mari was glad to do it, and I was glad to go with her.

After a hearty breakfast of French toast, we set off. I read the list aloud as Mari drove.

"Three lipsticks, one called "summer rose" and two called "raspberry." Four jars of cleansing cream. Some rouge for three women. Mari, we are going to have to find a place in town that has a big make-up section."

Mari nodded. "If you look on the back of the list, you'll see that he also wrote down the names of the stores."

She glanced at me, a mischievous grin on her face. "Hearing that list, I can't help but think that Father Hunt is a hero for doing this shopping!"

"Oh—Mari, on the list there is one ladies underslip, size 4, and even some underpants for women!"

We chuckled over this for a second, but then Mari said, "If we think this was hard for Father Hunt to have to go into stores and ask for these things, imagine how hard this is for the women who can't buy these embarrassing things for themselves and have to have a man buy them!"

That brought the mood down pretty quickly.

We were silent for a moment, and I remembered, "Alice told me her mother uses beet root juice for lipstick."

Mari nodded. "People in the camps are pretty clever and creative."

Once in Tulelake, we shopped for four pairs of children's shoes. The clerk looked at us oddly. She knew we were too young to have children of our own. And besides, people usually brought kids into a store to get the shoes fitted. She gave us what we asked for, but she looked quite grim.

At the make-up counter, Mari read off her list. The clerk began gathering everything up. She was relaxed and friendly, but was curious about the large amount we were buying.

"Having a big make-up party at your house?" she asked.

"Something like that," Mari said, with a friendly smile.

"Have fun!" the clerk called after us.

The slip and underwear were a littler easier. Apparently teenaged girls can buy things like that for a mother or aunt. No questions were asked.

In a men's store, we requested two white dress shirts.

At first the clerk was friendly, but when we gave him the sizes, he looked at us sharply.

"If these are for your father, he must be a small man," he said.

As if it was any business of his, I thought. But I piped up, "They are for our brother."

"He wears two different sizes?" the man said. One eyebrow was raised and his voice was testy now.

Mari looked him and said, "And we will take both of them."

I knew I was out of my league. Mari felt no need to make up a story. I admired her grit. We got the shirts and walked out of that store.

But Mari really shone when it came to buying the Dixie Peach Hair Pomade.

This was all the rage with young men. It was a thick, gooey gel that held hair in place, and gave it a shine. If you have seen movies with Rudolph Valentino or Cary Grant, you would know how cool it was.

We walked up to the counter and Mari said politely, "Dixie Peach Hair Pomade, please."

The man behind the counter looked at her. Then at me, and then back at Mari. There was no 'how can I help you?' attitude here.

"What do you want with Dixie Peach Hair Pomade?" he asked suspiciously. "Only the Japs in the camp use that."

"Oh, really?" Mari said casually. "Well, I want four jars."

"Well, maybe I'll give it to you and maybe I won't," he said. He crossed his arms across his chest.

Then he just stood there, looking at her, daring her to argue with him.

I got really nervous. But I remembered the other store and remained silent.

Mari also remained silent. She just stared right back at him with her big, dark eyes. And that stare had power. She had said her piece and not another word escaped from her.

Her attitude unnerved the guy. He went and got the hair gel.

I was relieved when we had paid and could leave. Mari walked out of the story with dignity—and with four jars of Dixie Peach Pomade!

From there we headed off to buy the lemon drops for Mrs. Ikejeri and some newspapers to read back in our barracks.

On the drive back, we were quiet. I watched the California countryside and thought how proud I was of Mari.

The newspapers we brought back from Tulelake were a big hit in our quarters. On Sunday afternoon after church, we sat around the table, all reading different sections.

Dad was sitting back in his chair, but suddenly he sat up straighter. "There is a photograph here of an army general presenting a medal, the Distinguished Service Cross, to a young woman whose brother was killed in Italy last year. He was one of four brothers from that family who were serving in the military. They are Japanese-Americans.

"The brother who died, Kazuo Masuda, was an amazing hero. He was part of the 442nd Regimental Combat Team."

Wasn't that the same regiment that Tomi's brother, Yosh, was in? But I didn't interrupt Dad as he continued reading to us.

"At one time, Kazuo Masuda and his men were under heavy fire. He ordered them back to safety. Then by himself, he fought the Nazis for 12 hours! Several weeks later, in Cassino, Italy, he attempted to do something like that again. That is when he was killed."

Dad read a little more to himself and then said, "Apparently the general went to the family's farm to personally honor the young man.

"Here is the history behind this story: The father of the family had been imprisoned soon after the bombing of Pearl Harbor, as so many men were, and the rest of the large family was incarcerated in a relocation center, except the four sons who had joined the army. Now that the war is over, the family was recently released from the relocation camp and returned home. They were very lucky in that their farm was still intact and had not been taken over by others. But, they soon were threatened by other locals who did not want the family to return."

There were several reactions among us at the table.

"Can you imagine having four sons all fighting in the war?"

"How proud and profoundly sad they must be!"

"But shouldn't the family have been honored in Washington D.C.?"

"But at least that general made a big deal out of their loss."

Dad listened to our remarks. Then he added, "War makes for incredibly crazy and unfair situations. Think about this: the son who died was being honored, and the family was receiving this honor; but the general, who traveled to their home to show his condolences and respect to the family, was not allowed by army rules to pin the medal onto the mother of the soldier.

"This was because she was not an American citizen and was considered an 'enemy alien.' But the country her son died for had laws saying she couldn't become an American citizen!

"So she stood there while the general pinned it on the sister of the man who died, who then in turn took it off and pinned it onto her mother."

Yes, we all agreed that was crazy and unfair. That is what war does to people. There wasn't much more to say. We had to live with our frustrations.

"My obaa-san wants you to come see her," Alice said one day at school. "She wants to show you what she and my mother have been making!"

I mentioned this to my mother as I always told her where I would be after school each day.

"It sounds like you have become someone Alice's grandmother can talk to," Mom said.

I giggled. "Well, she speaks Japanese and I speak English, but I guess we sort of talk to each other."

"How?" Larry asked.

I remembered the day when Alice had showed me the brooches made of shells and how her grandmother had understood I loved flowers. She had held my hand and looked into my eyes.

"I guess we talk through our hearts," I said.

Of course Mom said I could visit Alice and her grandmother. I walked into their cramped quarters and saw a beautiful bouquet sitting on the table. It was winter, but I had the urge to go right up to it and stick my nose into the flowers because they looked so real.

"Oh!" I exclaimed. "Irises, and sweet peas! Lilacs! Oh these are so beautiful!"

Alice's grandmother and mother were both smiling.

"But how did you make these?" I asked.

Alice's mother spoke English, but she clearly wanted her mother to take the credit for the bouquet. She translated my words into Japanese.

Again through translation, I learned that they had saved colorful pages from magazines and the colored paper liners from apple crates! What talent and patience it must have taken to create something so lovely and realistic out of scrap paper!

"They seem so real!" I said. "It is like you have a summer garden on your table!"

After a little more translation, we could all laugh together.
But in our hearts, we had already understood.

We knew the barracks walls were thin, but we really
understood that when Mom asked from the bedroom, "Mari,
what time is it?"

Before Mari could answer, the woman in the next barracks
called, "It's just 6 o'clock, dearie!"

We looked at each other for a moment and burst out
laughing.

But we certainly never talked about our neighbors after
that!

Tomiko and I were alone in the kitchen in my quarters. I
was making us sandwiches and humming "We Wish You a
Merry Christmas."

I was a little early on the Christmas carols, but I was
enjoying myself.

Our books were spread out on the table already. The late
afternoon sun was coming through the window. I loved how
the sunshine looked at this time of year, so low and soft. It
made me feel all Christmasy.

Tomi did not seem happy, though.

Her family was Buddhist, so they did not celebrate
Christmas. I wondered if my humming Christmas songs was
bothering her.

I decided to ask because that seems like the best way to be
a friend.

"What's wrong, Tomi? Do you want to talk?"

I was right. She did want to talk, because when Tomi began,
it was like a dam breaking. Words rushed out of her so fast, I
was startled.

"Things are just awful for our family! Mom and Dad are
both so sad. You know my dad had a really great store for years.

He's used to working hard and being busy. He used to manage everybody and tell us what to do and gave us all whatever we needed. But now the government tells everybody what to do, even him," she said.

Tomi was not usually a crier but I heard a catch in her throat. "It's like he isn't needed or even worse—like he hardly exists."

"What do you mean?" I asked, but Tomi didn't explain that. I guess she had so much more to say.

"We don't do things together as a family anymore. We don't even eat together. Mom can't cook the kind of food we're used to. She feels bad because she thinks she isn't a good mother," she said.

Tears were streaming down her cheeks now. "We eat in the mess hall and the food is awful stuff we've never eaten or even seen before. With the long tables we don't even sit together. We kids sit with our friends and my parents sit with the other grown-ups."

I listened. I didn't know what else to do.

"We don't even really talk anymore as a family. Every night, we just crawl into our lumpy straw sacks at night to sleep like dogs in a kennel," she said, not looking at me, or anything else in particular.

When we were at Amache, I had learned about those lumpy sacks stuffed with straw. These served as mattresses. When the internees had arrived, they were given big cloth bags to stuff with straw. They even had to do the stuffing themselves.

If that wasn't miserable enough, they lay down on those wretched sacks in a room that was only about 10 by 12 feet, and freezing cold. And when they turned off the one single light bulb hanging down from the ceiling, the searchlights would penetrate the windows.

Tomi was really crying now. Her shoulders were shaking. I sat down at the table beside her. I wondered if, in her crowded space with her family, she ever let herself cry like this.

My mind, however, began wandering around in an angry place, a place I seemed to be visiting more and more.

What the government was doing showed their contempt for these Americans. It showed their complete lack of respect for them as human beings with families and with intellects and God-given souls.

They seemed to think of them as unimportant animals that had to be put someplace and just kept alive like cows in a barn or junk stored in a warehouse until you decide what to do with it at some later date.

When I came out of this anger, Tomi was still crying. I put my arm around her and continued to sit there.

We were still there and Tomi was still crying when Mari came in a few moments later. She asked no questions, but tossed off her coat, came over to the table and put her arms around both of us.

I remember thinking she smelled of fresh air.

Both Mom and Dad worked long hours now. When they did come home, they each looked exhausted and worried.

Every day they faced the problems of many people, and there were no quick answers. Sometimes there were no answers at all.

I struggled to understand how this questionnaire and its loyalty questions had caused so many problems. I listened and asked questions and I think this is what happened:

Some of the internees went ahead and signed, but for different reasons. There were others who couldn't or wouldn't sign it.

The "Couldn'ts" were mostly old people who were not allowed to become American citizens. Their Japanese citizenship was all they had! The oath required that you renounce all allegiance to any other country but the United

States. But the United States had declared long ago that it would never let them become citizens.

You could easily see why they couldn't sign. If they gave up their Japanese citizenship they would be stateless. That meant they would have no citizenship in any country on earth.

A person simply can't exist that way. You have to belong to some country.

If I knew that and I was only 12 years old, you would think our government would know it too!

Now we come to the "Wouldn't" people, the ones who didn't sign and things get more complicated.

Another part of the oath was to swear that you would fight for the U.S. in our military. Many young men, like Yosh, were already doing this.

These soldiers were fighting bravely for the country that was imprisoning their families, but they still loved the United States and wanted to prove that they are loyal to it.

But other young men were angry and said "no" to the question for that very same reason. Soon they were called the "No No's." Most of them, like Jiro, loved the United States too but felt that they simply had to make a statement that what was happening to them and their families was wrong.

Because she worked in the hospital, Mom got to know many of the oldest people in camp. She explained to me that some of these people honestly believed that Japan had won the war!

A couple of years ago, they had been told that they would have to go back to Japan when the war was over. Now it was over, and these people believed that they were going to their long-ago home, which had recently won a war.

Maybe they thought this because no radios were allowed in the camps. We never got to hear any news broadcasts. No newspapers delivered to the camp, either—which is why Mari and I bought some in Tulelake. Keeping up with the war news was almost impossible.

Maybe because they hadn't known what was happening, and were convinced they were to be sent to Japan, they convinced themselves it would be OK.

But it wasn't just about them. They had children and grandchildren. The elders put very strong pressure on the young people in their families to renounce, which meant to give up, their U.S. citizenship!

I knew that in most Japanese families, kids were brought up to respect and obey their elders in ways that were stronger and more involved than what I had seen in other families.

So this put the younger generations in a horrible bind. If the elders left for Japan, they would have to go too.

Dad told me that many of the young people had given up their U.S. citizenship because of their grandparents' needs and were now regretting it. They came to Dad to try to get their citizenship restored. This was very hard to do. He was afraid it might even be impossible.

So now people from the Department of Justice were arriving at Tule Lake Segregation Center. They were holding hearings to decide who could get their citizenships back and who wouldn't.

That is why Dad was working day and night, or a least very late into the evenings. He was trying to get these young men ready for their hearings.

Dad is not usually a forceful person, but when he sees a wrong, he goes full-force to try to right it, and you'd better stay out of his path or you're going to get mowed down! I knew he would work as hard as he could to help.

One morning I talked to him about Yosh and Jiro, and about the young men that jogged past our quarters at dawn, chanting and exercising. Larry joined us.

"Try to imagine that you have been forced to live in this prison, for all of your high school years. You had done nothing wrong, and you have had to watch your grandparents, your parents, your sisters and brothers all suffer in so many ways.

You don't know if you will get to graduate from high school, and if you will ever get to college or get any kind of job training. You don't even know if you and your family will have a home to go to if ever you get out of here."

Dad paused, letting that sink in. "Your parents or grandparents are preparing to go back to Japan. Even though you are an American and may never have even been to Japan, they are putting pressure on you to come with them. And you don't want your family separated either. Also, you know that 'out there,' white people will look at you as if you have done something wrong. Everything you will have to do when you get out to set up your life again will be made harder still by this prejudice."

"So some, like Yosh, decide going into the army is the best way to fit in?" I asked.

"Very possibly," Dad said, "though of course I can't speak for Yosh."

"And Jiro is doing what we are taught in school—that in America, one way to change a bad situation is to peacefully protest. He is protesting by not signing the questionnaire," Larry said.

"And the young men—and the young women too—who are working to learn to speak Japanese better and learning about that culture right now, and even doing their exercises?" I asked. "What about them?"

"They see going to Japan is the only way for them. They know they will face even more prejudice in the United States than they did before the war. They have no money or home. And, their parents are saying they must come with them to Japan," Dad said. "They have lost any faith in the United States."

"And maybe they are tired of feeling like being Japanese is bad," I said. "Maybe they want to be able to feel proud of who they are."

Dad gave me one of those, "You got it" looks.

And Larry had got it too. He said. "I will go on with my life as a white kid who doesn't have to face any of these things. Most likely my future is a lot brighter than theirs."

I looked at Dad. He was proud of both of us, and worried about all the kids who were in such a bad situation.

He put his coffee cup into the sink and said, "Well, I'd better get to work."

I told Alice and Tomi about my trips to the town of Tulelake with Mari. We had gone about three times now.

As usual, we were all at my quarters because it was bigger than Tomi's or Alice's places.

"There always seems to be something on our shopping list that causes some clerks to look at us as if we are people they can't trust," I said.

Tomi looked right at me. "Does that look make you feel like you are bad or have done something wrong?"

I was not sure what she meant. "Well, I haven't done anything wrong. I was just trying to buy something in a store, just like anyone else."

"Yes, but when a clerk looks at you that way, as if you can't be trusted, does it make you feel bad about yourself?"

Confused, I said again, "Well, I know I haven't done anything to deserve that."

Tomi looked at Alice. Alice looked at Tomi. There was a look between them that I didn't understand.

Tomi shrugged and sat back.

Alice piped up. "So what happens in the stores?"

I told them about the questioning looks anytime we went to buy something that wasn't obviously for ourselves. The lemon drops were fine. The clothing in a variety of sizes often led to questions. And the hair pomade always meant we would be challenged by some clerk.

"Even so, you and Mari always manage to buy the things on the list," Alice said. "So how do you deal with the people who question you or are rude to you?"

So I told them about Mari.

Of course, they had met her many times. But I told them about the Mari who digs in her heels and won't be moved. This is especially true when there is something that she thinks is wrong. She is fearless.

"My mom says that from the time Mari was little she has always tried to 'fix' anything bad or unhappy or wrong. She sees it and she charges into battle with banners flying," I said and then had to laugh. "I think if Joan of Arc had had a little sister, I know exactly how she would have felt. I admire Mari's courage and I wish I were more like her. She charges forward, and I just stand there with my mouth open in awe."

"You are the reserve troops, not usually on the front line?" Alice asked, a teasing look in her eyes.

We both laughed, but Tomi was looking puzzled. "Joan of who?"

"Joan of Arc," I said.

"She is a saint," Alice said. "A really, really brave one."

"And she was a girl, a teenager, who did what she felt was right," I said.

"And died because of it," Alice added.

"Well, I don't suppose anything like that will happen to Mari. But how does Mari get these people to give in?" Tomi asked.

"Mari will just stand there staring at them. She says what she needs to say and then not another word escapes her. She has the biggest, darkest brown eyes and a look that Queen Victoria would have envied. In the end the clerks always cave in and she gets everything she came for. I love to see her do this, but because I have rather light blue eyes, I would never try it. It would never work."

I said this and then realized that both of my friends had dark eyes too. We all laughed again.

Then Alice said, "But how does she ever have the nerve to do that?"

"I guess she was sort of born that way," I mused. "Mari is exactly like my dad. He has a way of staying quiet when the rest of us are talking about something important. Then he will say something that sums it all up. Immediately, everybody's ears perk up.

"People just seem to listen to him and respect him. I've seen this and I know where Mari gets it. They both have this way of seeing something that is wrong. Then they seem to get this absolute necessity to see that right is done. Mari also has the gift of saying it and stopping. She doesn't 'chew it to death,' as Larry would put it."

"And what about you?" Tomi asked.

"I'm like Mom. We are both more followers than leaders. We get a lot done though."

"Ever since I met you, I have wondered if your mom wanted to come to this place," Alice said.

"Yes, I think she did. She loves our home and her garden, but Mom is always 100 percent behind Dad. She agrees with what he sees is necessary almost all the time. They just have the same beliefs, I guess. Mom always finds her own way to do things, though."

"Do you feel like Mari is stronger than you?" Tomi asked.

"Mari is braver than I, but I'm not a scaredy-cat. I can be as brave as I have to be. But I don't go around looking for situations the way Mari does," I said, and then I remembered something.

"I'll tell you about the time we were living somewhere else far away and we thought German planes were coming to bomb our little town. I was all alone due to a mix-up and I was only 9, but I remember being cool as a cucumber. I thought, if they're coming they're coming and there's nothing I can do to stop them. And why get upset when there was nobody around to comfort me."

"What happened?" Alice asked.

"Well, since I'm still here, you know it was a false alarm. And the German planes never came there at all, thank God."

"Good for you for being so brave!" Tomi said. "Hooray for Helen!"

Yes, I thought. Hooray for me!

That was a fun afternoon. I offered to walk my friends back to their barracks.

We were laughing again as we trudged through the winter cold. When we passed one of the public bathrooms, a woman came out. I glanced at her and before the door slammed shut, I caught a glimpse of the inside.

There were no stalls like you would see in a public restroom! There were no curtains either. Just a long row of what looked like a bench with sides on it. Where a person would sit down on the bench, there was a hole. Several holes, in the seat of this long bench.

I suddenly realized: this bench was actually a toilet, or several toilets!

"You have no privacy at all in the bathroom!" I said, stunned.

Both Alice and Tomi looked at me with a look that said. "You are just figuring that out now?" But I had to keep asking.

"You just sit next to someone while you are both peeing?" I asked.

I think the word I need to describe how I was feeling was "incredulous."

"Yes, and not just pee, poop too," Alice said frankly. "Sometimes you bump shoulders when there are more than two of you."

"We girls have created our own privacy, though," Tomi said. "We have a paper bag with eye holes that we put over our head when we have to 'go.' People can see us, but they don't know who we are."

That should not have to be anybody's idea of privacy! It wouldn't work for showering either!

Just how many people had to use each of these bathrooms, I wondered. Perhaps if there were plenty of these bathrooms, you could sometimes get to pee all by yourself.

So I asked.

"For every block of 10 barracks, there are two, one for women and one for men," Alice said.

My mind reeled as I tried, and failed, to do the math. Each block of barracks had different-sized rooms and the number of people in a room varied. Impossible to know how many lived there, but it was a lot of people. That was certain.

"And I thought it was crazy that our neighbor can hear everything we say, but to share a bathroom that has no stalls....!" I said.

"It was really hard at first. It's still hard, but you do get less embarrassed after awhile," Alice said. "Though one day, I saw my obaa-san coming out of the bathroom and she had tears on her cheeks."

Sweet, artistic, dignified Obaa-san. My heart ached.

This was not a pleasant conversation. Yet, Tomi started to laugh. "We hear everything in our barracks too. I often listen to a mother singing a lullaby to her baby. And I have heard a grandfather scolding a toddler and a boy and girl make a secret date—something I knew their parents would never allow! And arguments, lots of arguments. It is hard to live with so many people so close together."

Nodding, Alice said, "I have heard families singing 'happy birthday.' People reading letters out loud. A dad telling a bedtime story. Women weeping. Lots of talk about the loyalty questions."

Tomi said, "Lots and lots of talk about the loyalty questions. I have heard young men sobbing and men praying." Then she added, "If someone throws up at night, we all hear that too. We hear everything."

But Alice was not going to dwell on this topic. "It is getting closer to Christmas!" she said cheerfully. "And I have an idea for a surprise for my family!"

She would not tell Tomi and me what it was, no matter how hard we tried to pry her secret out of her!

Walking back by myself, I thought a lot about privacy. I also gave more thought to bodily functions on that walk than I ever had before.

I thought of the indignity and misery of having to throw up, even in a warm house with a clean bathroom. But feeling so sick and then trying to run to the public bathroom....

I thought about trying to help a toddler figure out potty-training.

I thought about girls getting their periods.

I thought about a woman close to having a baby, so having to pee more often.

Privacy and bathrooms were very important!

But what bothered me the most was the image of Alice's dear grandmother, crying as she left the public bathroom.

The internees were not some grubby little creatures that someone dug up from underground! They were refined, well-educated people from homes that may have been nicer than the home we left.

These were people with university degrees, probably better educated than many of their "keepers."

There were successful businessmen, doctors, lawyers, teachers and artists. And no matter what their education or income, they were still good people, who kept a house and made it a home and loved their families.

This is not what any child of God deserves!

And every person in this camp was a child of God.

Sometimes, when I am angry, I pray. And that is what I did the rest of the way back.

Even though Mom was working long hours at the hospital, she still offered to fix Father Hunt's coat. And she had to do so about once a week, because it was so unbelievably shabby.

This coat was so old and worn that when she brought it home, it was in two or even three pieces! She managed to sew it back into one piece every time. She used heavy thread and fervent prayers to whoever is the patron saint of seamstresses. I don't know how she was even able to put it back together. It's like that stupid joke, "Would you please sew a shirt on my button?" His overcoat is about reduced to "button" status. Which is funny to say because it actually didn't even have buttons anymore!

As she sewed, she told me that during her days at the hospital, she often heard how much people in camp loved Father Hunt. "They tell me he is so warm and willing to help anyone. They tell of different ways he has helped their families. And they marvel and say that no matter if they are Catholic, Protestant, Buddhist or atheist, he is there for them."

"I guess He wants them to know that God loves everybody, even the ones who don't love Him back. Maybe they just don't know who He is yet," I said. "Hey, Mom, guess what!"

She looked up at me, interest in her eyes.

"I've learned to recite the whole 'Hail Mary' in Japanese. I'm so proud of myself!"

And then I proceeded to say the ancient prayer to God's mother, so familiar to my family in English.

Mom listened. "I am so impressed, Helen! That is wonderful! And how wonderful to be able to pray in two languages!"

I nodded happily. Mari was speaking lots of Japanese now. Languages came so easy to her, but not to me.

My wise mother knew I was comparing myself to Mari. She snipped off the end of the thread and said, "That really is terrific, Helen. We all have our gifts. Each of our accomplishments is something to be proud of."

Yes, I thought. I have struggled and I did it. Hooray for me!

I told my mom about Tomi's concern about her family.

"She really cried a lot," I said. "She doesn't usually talk about her feelings much. I didn't know what to say."

"Tomi's family is under so much stress, Helen. Just being here would be enough stress for any family, but you add their not knowing if they will get their home and jobs back, and then, the worry about her brother who is in the war," Mom said, handing me the vegetable peeler and a bowl of potatoes. "Just being with her and listening if she wants to talk will be a big help to her."

We agreed I should ask Tomi over after school again soon.

Two days later, Larry came home with Tomi and me, grabbed a few apples and headed out to play basketball with some friends, boys who lived near Alice.

Once again, Tomi and I had the place to ourselves. I planned to say something so she might feel like she could talk with me about her worries again if she wanted to.

I made us some cocoa and took it into the bedroom where Tomi was sitting on my bed. She was reading a magazine with her back to me.

"It must have been really hard to come here," I said, feeling a little weird about starting the conversation.

Tomiko turned around. I thought she was going to cry but instead she burst out, "Can you imagine leaving home, maybe forever, carrying only what you can fit into one suitcase?

"Think about it. Stand in your room and decide what to take. Or rather, take what your mom has told you to pack, shoes, underwear, pj's, toiletries. No room for any of your treasures," she said. "You might even need to make room for some of your baby brother's diapers. And where are your other clothes? They're on you in five or six layers. You are wearing everything you can and still be able to move. Even though it's a warm spring day your winter coat has to go on top of everything else and you have to wear your winter boots because they would take too much space in the only suitcase you can bring."

I tried to imagine. Of course, I didn't have very much here, but once again I thought about my room back home in Park Ridge. I could barely stand the thought of losing it all forever.

I could picture my maple spindle bed with the quilted bedspread Grandma made. Again I longed for the handmade dollhouse with all the little furniture that Grandpa made the year before he died. If our house caught fire, my dollhouse would be the first thing I would grab. Then there are all my books, my dolls, the pictures on the walls that great aunt Sarah painted so long ago....

Suddenly I understood what Tomiko and her family had gone through better than I ever had before.

She was almost shaking, but the outburst was over. I said, "Tomi, I'm so proud of you. You are so strong, so brave. I could never do what you did."

In a quiet voice, she said, "Yes you could if you had absolutely no other choice. We are all strong and brave when we have to be. All of the Japanese on the West Coast had to do exactly the same thing.

"What I lost was nothing compared to the people who lost houses, stores, professions, businesses, farms—even their cars or trucks. They had worked their whole lives for these things that supported their families. And they were afraid that they would probably never get any of it back. But there was nothing else to do. What else could any of us do?"

Of course I had no answer so I just sat down on the bed too. She seemed calmer now.

We sipped our cocoa as I struggled to think of what to say next but Tomi solved that for me.

"Let's do our homework and get it over with," she said.

When Tomi left, I watched her from the window. She walked down the road, her head held high. No one else seeing her would suspect the pain she was carrying.

I had noticed this amazing spirit of acceptance among the people in the centers before. I tried and tried to understand it.

There were people here at Tule Lake who had fought for their rights. But they had not been violent—though some had been treated violently. In general, no one was sulking and pouting either. They are behaving with this incredible dignity and acceptance.

When someone is always treated badly, do they become used to it?

In the United States, we had heard a little that the Nazis were imprisoning Jewish people in Europe, and some other groups too. Could it be that the Japanese-Americans were both a little bit afraid and a little bit thankful that it wasn't worse than it was for them?

And Tomi was right: what else could they do? Go to war against the U.S. Army? There were only about 120,000 people of Japanese ancestry, and that wasn't all young able-bodied people. That included old men and women, little kids and babies. No match for the army! They did the only thing they could do and survive: go along with the imprisonment.

By now, I had learned a little about Japan and what it meant to be someone whose family was from there. It was a small, crowded country. Just to survive, good manners and self-restraint were probably necessary. You couldn't go running around wildly or even acting out your feelings. You might disturb and maybe even hurt the people around you.

That got me to thinking about what it means to live in the United States, a country whose background is very different from Japan's.

In our country with its wide open spaces, we did not have as strong a sense of self-restraint and manners. We can be very nice people, of course, but here a lot of people think that speaking up and expressing yourself is a good thing.

I guessed it had to do with how our government had been set up too.

Then I thought about religion. Many of the people here were Buddhists. Did Buddhists think that if you are in unpleasant circumstances the best thing for you to do is to ignore the circumstances rather than try to improve them? I kind of thought so, but I wasn't certain.

My family, who was Christian, didn't believe that at all. We thought that God wants us to try to help out and to improve the situation both for ourselves and especially for helpless people around us.

I thought maybe that was why we had been in this war now. We couldn't just ignore what Hitler was doing. I wondered about all of this.

It occurred to me then that Tomi and I were both born in the United States but we came from very different cultures.

The door opened. Larry came in with his three basketball teammates. They were in high spirits, laughing and teasing each other.

Together they started making sandwiches. As they wolfed down their snack, I thought that the differences between our two cultures weren't so clear when it came to hungry teenaged boys!

My mother had not forgotten that some orphaned children had been placed in one of the relocation camps. Dad had heard about this when we were still at Amache, but he had not learned much more. So now she asked a lot of questions at work and came home with information.

She also came home with Father Hunt's coat, this time in three pieces.

"Most of the children who were in orphanages in Los Angeles and San Francisco are now in a camp in California called Manzanar. They have created a special section for orphans there," she told me. "A social worker and her husband, both of whom are Japanese-American and would have been interned too, volunteered to go with all these children and care for them."

Somehow the idea of kids, who were already growing up in orphanages, being taken away by soldiers to one of these centers horrified me.

"So those are the people who are with the kids there?" I asked, wanting good news. "I bet they are taking good care of them."

Mom nodded distractedly and began to sew Father Hunt's coat back together.

That evening, Father Hunt came over. As usual, we gathered around the table for cocoa and talk. First we discussed ideas for the Christmas Eve services. Soon I was hopeful that it would feel Christmasy after all.

Mom then asked if Father Hunt knew anything about orphaned children in a relocation camp called Manzanar.

"Oh, yes, I do. Some Maryknoll Sisters had an orphanage in Los Angeles for children of Japanese ancestry," he told us.

"At the Maryknoll orphanage, they had 33 children. Some were Japanese, some had only one Japanese parent and a parent from a different group of people, but no family to care for them.

"Some parents couldn't care for the children because one parent was put into a center that did not take children but the other parent was sick with tuberculosis and in a hospital—in a case like that, the child wasn't able to go with either parent. There were all sorts of situations.

"One little girl called Annie had been brought to the orphanage as a premature infant. She did not have any family members to care for her. When she arrived, she weighed only two pounds and was sick with pneumonia!"

Mom gasped. Only two pounds and pneumonia were very serious things for babies!

"But they fed and loved her, gave her the medicines she needed. Annie got well and she blossomed into a rosy 3 year-old. And then came the order for all Japanese on the West Coast to be imprisoned in camps."

There was a look of horror on Mom's face. "I can't believe the government could actually have been worried about little children in orphanages!"

Father Hunt nodded wearily and went on, "As soon as the sisters heard about this, they acted immediately. They learned if they could place these children in another area, away from the West Coast, they wouldn't have to go to the prison camps."

"What did they do then?" I asked.

"What they didn't do was wait for orders from the army," he said. "Instead they worked very hard to find foster homes for the children in places outside of the evacuation zone. They quickly contacted lots of people they thought could help."

"When the soldiers arrived at the orphanage to take the little ones to Manzanar, there were only seven left. The sisters had managed to place 26 in homes away from the West Coast.

"Of course, this meant that the only security these children had, which was the sisters and the orphanage, was taken from them as they were sent off. Still, it was better than going into a prison camp."

I thought I'd like to meet those sisters who had managed to keep twenty-six kids out of the camps!

"And the other seven?" asked Larry.

"I heard it was a pretty tearful time when the soldiers arrived and forced the sisters to give up the others."

We were all silent for a moment.

But Father Hunt had more to tell us. "There were two other orphanages with kids of Japanese descent. The people who ran those orphanages also fought to help their children. But the government was fierce in its round-up. In the end, the children from those places, along with the seven from Maryknoll, ended up in Manzanar."

Now it was Mom who nodded wearily.

"Little children without families!" Mari fumed, "What possible threat could they be to our country?"

Larry said, "The government must be afraid that they would throw their teddy bears at people and cause gross bodily harm!"

It was funny, but not funny at all.

Mom looked as if she were going to cry. "And little Annie?? She was only 3 years old!"

"I think she was one of the seven who had to go to Manzanar," Father Hunt said.

"A 3-year-old?"

"Some of the children sent there were as young as 6 months old."

"You can't be a spy or a traitor when you can't even crawl yet," Mari said.

"This shows just how crazy people can get when they are fearful. There was so much fear after the bombing of Pearl Harbor," Dad said. "And of course, others used that fear to do evil."

He had been silent for all this time, and he looked discouraged.

"Little by little, I am learning more about that," Father Hunt said. "Another Maryknoll priest, Father Hugh Lavery, contacted the army. He wanted to know what would happen to these children without families.

"He got a letter from a Colonel Karl R. Bendetsen, in Washington, D.C. It read something like, 'I am determined that if they have one drop of Japanese blood in them, they must go into a camp.'"

I felt sort of sick. What kind of person could feel like that towards a little child?

"So how are these children being cared for at Manzanar?" Dad asked.

"There is a separate place within the center, called The Children's Village. I guess they made it a little nicer than the centers in general. There is a playground there and some fruit trees were planted within it. And the buildings at least have running water and toilets."

Mom said, "Well, for the adults caring for all those children, there had better be running water and toilets!"

"How many children are there?" Mari asked.

"I think that they ended up with about 100," Father Hunt said.

Larry gave a low whistle. "That is a lot of responsibility," he said quietly.

I sat there, thinking about not having a family and living in an orphanage, and then having soldiers come and take you away on a train and putting you into a place like this.

It seemed the more we learned about this whole "evacuation," the more crazy it appeared. I wondered if people would be still shocked by this a few years from now.

I must have looked upset, because Father Hunt stood up to leave and said, "I did hear one thing that lifted my spirits, though."

We all seemed to sit up straighter at these words!

"I was told that there is a teenaged boy who lives with his family in Manzanar. His name is John Sohei Hohri. His barracks is quite near the Children's Village. He has taken to helping the little orphans in a very special way. He comes to the Children's Village each evening, to the room where there are 14 small boys, each in pajamas and lying on folding cots. He tells them bedtime stories! There are very few children's books there, so he apparently tiptoes around the room and acts out the stories he tells."

We all smiled a little. It was good to hear something delightful among all the pain and sadness.

"Well, it is getting late. Thank you, Nelle, for your weekly sewing job! I appreciate it more than I can say!" Father Hunt said. He picked up his coat, once again in one piece, and set off into the darkness.

As I brushed my teeth, I wondered how those seven children were doing at Manzanar with other orphaned kids.

And where were the 26 children who had left before the soldiers came? Not in prison, which was very good. But where did they end up? Who was caring for them? Only time would tell how this move would change their lives.

I thought of Tomomi, Itsuo and Mikiko. It was very strange to think of them as being lucky. But they had two parents and two grandparents taking care of them.

I turned out the bathroom light and headed to bed.

Sometimes I just couldn't figure life out at all.

"Come see my Christmas tree!" Alice invited Tomi and me. "How about tomorrow?"

"A Christmas tree?" Tomi was astounded. "How did you get a tree?"

I wondered too. The closest thing to a Christmas tree around here was some scrubby little plant that I thought was called sagebrush. And of course, Alice's parents weren't allowed out of the camp to go buy a Christmas tree.

But Alice's eyes sparkled. "Just wait and see!"

I told my mother about Alice's announcement. Smiling, Mom said, "I am very curious and want to hear all about it!"

So after school the next day, the three of us girls set off for Alice's barracks.

Tomi and I tried to get Alice to tell us more. But Alice just giggled and ran ahead a little in her excitement.

We arrived to find Alice's mother and grandmother sewing at the little table. They were glad to see us, and Obaa-san again took my hands in hers for a moment and smiled at me.

And there was the Christmas tree. From green construction paper, Alice had cut out a shape of an evergreen tree. She had taped it to the wall. She must then have spent a lot of time making decorations, because the tree was covered with stars, balls, bells, candy canes and angels cut from papers of a variety of colors.

Alice looked at us, expecting us to be thrilled. Tomi smiled her big, radiant smile and said it was really lovely.

All of a sudden, I wanted to cry.

The feeling was very strong, but Alice was so happy that I was desperate to sound enthusiastic. Besides, I had no Idea why I was feeling the way I did. I wiggled my toes in my shoes, and bit my bottom lip in an effort to keep the tears from falling.

Alice's mother put her arm around her daughter. "Alice saved up her money for a few months to buy the paper and then secretly made the tree for us. Isn't it wonderful? We came back here from lunch a couple of days ago to this! "

"What a great idea, Alice," Tomi said. "You are so clever—just like your grandmother!"

I had gotten control of those tears now. "It is a wonderful surprise," I said.

Alice was beaming, she was so happy. I squeezed her hand.

I walked back to my quarters alone. It was dark as night comes on so early in December. I looked up at the starry sky and wondered why I had wanted to cry. Alice had made something for her family that had clearly made both her mother and grandmother happy. So why was I so sad?

Mom was just getting home from work and we entered the barracks together.

"Well, how was the Christmas tree?" Mom asked.

I told her—about the pretty paper tree, about how happy Alice was, and how I had come so close to crying. Mom sat down with me on the little couch.

"I think Alice surprising her family is wonderful," I blurted out and the tears began to flow. I could let them now. "I don't know why I'm so sad!"

Mom took my hand. "Helen, we aren't going to have a 'normal' Christmas this year either. What do you think you will miss about it?"

I just cried for a minute, and then I said, " Baking cookies, and being with cousins. The smell of a real Christmas tree. And getting out the ornaments that we put up every year on the tree. Setting up our crèche. Going to our church on Christmas Eve...I guess I am going to miss all that this year," I said. "That's why I am crying, I guess."

Silently, Mom sat with me and let me cry. Then she said, "It may not be as bleak a Christmas as you imagine, but I am wondering if some of your sadness is for Alice and all the other kids who are used to celebrating Christmas like you are. They haven't had a real Christmas for a few years now. And now they will have another Christmas without the things they love."

Startled, I looked at her. Yes—she had it right! I was sad for what I would miss but I was also sad for all the people here who were used to planning and enjoying Christmas or other holidays and who had been forced into this place and leave the joy behind.

Mari and I came home from our weekly shopping. Some of the families who celebrated Christmas had asked us to get a few things for their celebrations. No one had access to much money, so these were little things, like a few toys or art supplies, but it took longer than usual.

It was nice to be back with my family after the cold outside and the rudeness of some of the shop people.

Mom was once again sewing up Father Hunt's decrepit coat.

"Why doesn't he tell Maryknoll that he needs a new overcoat and to please send him some money?" I asked her.

Mom smiled. "I think he does. And I would guess they do send him the money. But then he sees someone here who needs it even more than he does and he uses the money for that."

Yup, I thought. That sums up Fr. Hunt to perfection.

It was a cold gloomy Saturday and I was walking towards the guardhouse that separates the colony from our side.

I was going to lend Tomi a book and spend a short time at her quarters. This guardhouse was our meeting place. I know that sounds a little strange, but everywhere you looked were low, colorless barracks and they all looked alike. The guard house was a midway point between her place and mine and easily seen.

Tomi was hurrying towards me. As we got closer, I realized that she was crying. For Tomi to be crying in public meant something was terribly wrong. I began running. I flew past the guardhouse without slowing. I knew it would be OK. They all knew Dad, and knew I was one of the Hannan kids.

I reached her and put my arms around her and asked, "Tomi, what's wrong? "

I probably had seen more of Tomi's emotions than most people, but I had never seen her like this, ever. She was sobbing so hard I couldn't understand her at all.

Fumbling for my handkerchief, I handed it to her and waited. I noticed we were near a low fence around a parking area, so I lead her there, to sit down with me.

Finally she was able to calm down. She mopped at her eyes. Taking a deep breath, she said, "We got a telegram from the army. Yosh was very badly wounded and they don't think he is going to live."

I remembered that Yosh was Tomi's oldest brother. I couldn't think of anything helpful or comforting to say so we just sat there and she began crying again. I put my arm around her, to comfort her and to keep us both a little warm. I could feel her whole body shaking. Eventually the sobbing slowed, but we stayed just as we were.

I thought about her brother Jiro, who was here in the camp. I also remembered that he had been really struggling to decide whether or not to sign the loyalty oath.

Yesterday I think he could have made a decision not to sign without looking back. But that telegram must have changed his whole world. He would be feeling that his family's honor needed him to take his brother's place. And family honor aside, he loved Yosh and would want to finish his dream for him.

As we sat there under the vigilant eyes of the army guard, I realized it was starting to get dark and we'd both better be getting home. But I felt she needed me to go with her. I was trying to be the steady rock she needed right now.

I stood up and took her hand. "Let's walk to your quarters," I said quietly.

As we approached her barracks, we saw that many neighbor men were standing outside with her father and Jiro. I followed Tomi inside.

Numerous women were there to support her mother, who was sitting on the floor, gently swaying back and forth with her eyes closed.

Tomi went over and knelt beside her and took her hand.

Following Tomi's lead, I knelt down in front of her but I had no idea what to say. So I fell back on my Irish grandmother's "I'm sorry for your trouble," which seems to cover any possible situation. I touched her arm and stood up and bowed and somehow backed out of the room as if I were leaving royalty.

Outside I nodded to Tomi's father whom I really didn't know. I looked up at Jiro and patted his arm. He smiled down at me. I hoped that he understood that I had some idea of the awful turmoil going on inside him and that I cared.

I was pretty certain he would make the decision for his family's honor and for his brother. He would carry it out with his whole soul and spirit, even if his heart wasn't completely there. That was the kind of person he was.

It was almost dark now so I ran all the way home, my shoes squeaking on the dirty snow. Mom was standing on the step watching for me. She must have heard the news about Yosh.

I flew in the door and threw myself into her arms and began to cry. I had used up my last grain of "Rock of Gibraltar" helping Tomi and now I was just a little girl who needed her mommy.

It was December 22, a day that usually gave me great joy because I loved Christmas. But this particular December 22, I was in the bedroom I shared with Mari, with a stuffy nose and a cough.

There had been no news of Tomi's brother, Yosh.

Feeling down, I started to read and was soon dozing.

I woke groggily, hearing that my parents were home from work. They were talking quietly and I heard the teakettle come to a boil.

My mom's voice sounded raspy. I think we were all sort of sick.

My dad said, "Here you are, my dear. A cup of tea."

There was a silence and I imagined Mom was sipping the tea. Then she asked Dad, "And what kinds of problems did you encounter today?"

I heard him sigh. "People worried about what will happen when they are released from here. Some of them may have to go to Japan, where they would really have no more life than we would if we suddenly had to go to the countries our ancestors left years ago.

"Others are looking for some certainty that they will be released even when this center closes. There is talk of some internees being further imprisoned in a place called Crystal City in Texas."

"Oh dear," Mom said. "That is the first I have heard of that."

"I am afraid there is more, Nelle. On Christmas Day, 1,800 people are scheduled to be taken to Portland to board a ship to Japan."

I started coughing then and the conversation ended there.

"Helen? I didn't realize you were home!" Mom called. "I thought you went to Alice's to bring her homework to her."

I came out of the bedroom. "I wasn't feeling well at the end of school today, so I just came back here. There wasn't any homework anyway."

Mom did her usual cool hand on my forehead and peering at my throat.

"You don't have a fever," Mom said.

"I don't feel really sick, just a little."

"Well, I have something for you to do here," Mom said. "Look what I have."

She handed me a box and I knew what was in it. I couldn't believe Mom had brought it with us from home.

I began unpacking it, and my parents watched with smiles on their faces. First I pulled out a newspaper-wrapped statue of Saint Joseph, then Mary. The next newspaper-covered figured had an odd shape and I knew it was the angel. After that came all the other figures from the Christmas story.

I happily spent the next hour setting up our little crèche.

It was Christmas Eve of 1945. Larry, Mari and Dad were all coughing along with Mom and me. Nobody was really ill, but with the prospect of people we knew being deported to war-ravaged Japan the next day, nobody was really well either.

"I wish there was something we could do!" Mari said, blowing her nose. "All these people being sent away!

At first no one said anything because we all knew there was nothing we could do about that. God knows Dad had done what he could.

Then Mom suggested, "Let's go to get a few groceries for Christmas."

"We could also get some gifts for people who are being deported, things they can put into their luggage," Larry suggested.

So the five of us piled into the big old car and drove through the gates.

Deep, gooey mud was everywhere in the little town, and we tried to avoid as much as we could as we went from store to store, stores which Mari and I knew well. There were quite a few last-minute gift buyers, who weren't finding what they wanted.

There wasn't much to find, with the war barely over. Mom had decided to get gloves for Fusa, a woman she worked with who would be on her way to Japan tomorrow. While she and Dad were searching for those, Mari, Larry and I were buying what few small toys we could find. We wanted to give at least some little kids a bit of Christmas.

It was a hungry, cold, and discouraged family that tromped through the mud back to our car.

Dad was coughing.

"I know what mud must feel like," Larry said.

We should have laughed at that, but no one did.

"We should have stayed in bed," Mom said, gloomily.

Back at Tule Lake, we saw people hurrying about, preparing to be deported.

Pulling off muddy boots, we got back into our barracks in lower spirits than when we had left.

Mari put a pot of Mom's soup onto the stove to heat. Soon we were at the table, enjoying the steaming liquid. And, you know, our spirits took off with that comforting liquid. It was, after all, Christmas Eve!

"Let's invite some of the kids who are leaving tomorrow. We can give them the gifts we just bought," Mari said.

It wasn't long before our barracks was filled with children who were happy with the small items we gave them. We sang Christmas carols and laughed and played.

Mom was smiling, holding a little one on her lap and chatting with others. Larry and Mari were on their hands and knees, being horses for the littlest kids. Dad was helping tie strings onto tops.

When it was time for them to leave, we gathered in the doorway to wave good-bye.

"Merry Christmas! Good-bye!" Mom called cheerily. But when the last of the children were out of hearing, she sighed.

"Dear Lord, please send your angels to shield and watch over these children in the years ahead," she prayed as we shut the door.

A light snow started to fall in the evening. Everything seemed fresh and almost cheerful. Dad packed up the crèche and we headed off with it to church.

Some of the people who went to the barracks/church had managed to decorate it so it looked a little festive. Larry and I made our contribution—the makeshift stable and statues. That added a lot.

Alice's father had come early and managed to get a fire going in the little potbelly stove, so it wasn't as cold as it usually was on Sundays.

Mari looked around for the small, portable organ. She had expected to be the organist as usual.

"Where's the organ?" I asked Mari.

She shrugged.

Father Hunt came in, dressed in his vestments for Mass. He saw Mari looking puzzled and came over to us.

"Thank you, Hannan family, for bringing tonight's focal point!" he said, gesturing to the crèche. "Sorry about the organ, Mari, but I am leaving very soon, and so I had to pack it."

"Where are you going?" Mari whispered back, surprised.

"To Japan as soon as possible. So tonight, we will have to sing a cappella!"

I was thinking about Father Hunt leaving and how that would affect everyone here. Then I remembered that hundreds of people would be leaving within the next few days too.

Before I could go further with those thoughts, the door opened and Alice, her mother and grandmother came in. I was so glad that family was not on a list for being sent to Japan!

Alice's mother was carrying the bouquet of exquisite flowers they had made of paper scraps.

Father Hunt hurried over to them, telling them in Japanese how much he appreciated them bringing this beauty. At least that is what Mari told me he was saying!

The door kept opening and people kept coming in. That drafty barracks was filling up and now it really felt like Christmas Eve services at home! There was that peculiar feeling you get only at Christmas of excitement and peace mixed together.

I was puzzled where all these people came from. It was an interesting assortment of races and places. Dad told me later he talked to someone who was from nearby Washington state and southern California and others from faraway Washington, D.C. and Maine.

And when we opened our mouths to sing, it felt like the whole world was singing together. We were amazing!

From the peaceful melody of "Silent Night" to the sweet images from the song, "Away in a Manger," we sang together, harmonizing as if we were a practiced choir.

People who were strangers, people who were family, people who had been imprisoned unfairly, people who were trying to help them, people who always went to church and people who had no church but wanted to be with others this night, people who were leaving, people who had just arrived—we stood shoulder to shoulder together on Christmas Eve, and sang with our voices and our souls.

During Mass, I thought of the newborn Jesus and his parents, forced to give birth in a stable and flee to another country soon afterwards. They were homeless and poor and had been treated unfairly.

If anyone would understand and love the people who would be leaving this camp, either to war-torn Japan or to California with both hopes and fears of what they would find there, it would be Jesus, the child born into a place as harsh and sad as this camp.

Our last song was about the humble shepherds getting the news of Jesus' birth from angels. It is an awesome thought and it is a song you really want to belt out! It always filled me with joy.

So along with everyone else in that miserable excuse for a church, I sang the carol that praises God:

"Angels we have heard on high,

sweetly singing o'er the plains,

and the mountains in rely,

echoing their joyous strains:

"Gloria, in excelsis Deo!

Gloria,in excelsis Deo!"

I looked around at all those singing souls and thought, "Yes! Glory to God in the highest!"

"I want to find Fusa, to give her the gloves I got for her. She will need them on the ship," Mom said.

It was Christmas Day, but the atmosphere outside our window was anything but festive. The snow had changed to a rainy drizzle so the sky was overcast. And the mud was back.

Hundreds of internees were packing up the few things they had and leaving the camp. But it was not a happy exit.

"Do you think you will find her, Mom? It looks like a lot of people have already left their barracks," Larry said. He was standing near the window.

Mari and I joined him.

Walking past our quarters was a steady stream of people. Mothers, fathers, grandparents, toddlers, teenagers, all carrying bags or babies or both.

"Larry's right, Mom," I said. "It will be hard to find her."

"Well then," said Mom. "I will pray to St. Anthony."

So, as she silently said words to the patron saint for finding lost things, she picked up the small package that contained the gloves for her co-worker, pulled on her boots and coat and started for the door.

"I'll go with you, Mom," I offered, even though I had never met Fusa and wouldn't be much help in finding her.

"Me too," said Larry.

"Me three," said Mari.

Dad already had his coat and boots on. We all needed to be out there. To say good-bye? To show support? I was not certain. But to have stayed in our warm barracks seemed uncaring. To be free people just because our ancestors had been born in Europe and not Japan didn't make us superior. We had to show we cared.

So we walked around in the mud and rain, among people who were leaving a terrible place for an uncertain future.

Babies were crying. Perhaps a lot of people were crying, but you couldn't tell the tears from the raindrops.

We just kept walking. Dad stopped every few minutes to shake hands or talk with someone he had met or worked with. Mom was straining to look for her friend, but also being stopped by people who wanted to hug her, to thank her for her help with an elderly parent in the hospital.

Doors kept opening and whole families emerged. Babies were strapped to backs of mothers. Toddlers were in the arms of grandfathers. Kids my age were hanging onto younger siblings.

I tried to imagine what it would be like if it were my family leaving for a ship that would take us to a place that had just lost a war.

There were so many people that Larry said, "Mom, I am not sure St. Anthony is your man today. I think you might need St. Jude."

Mari looked at me and rolled her eyes. St. Jude was the patron saint of lost causes. "That's really helpful, Larry," she said.

Mom didn't respond and Dad kept talking quietly with people he was powerless to help. After about a half hour, Mom suddenly cried out, "Fusa!"

A woman walking with a family turned. Her face looked careworn. But she smiled when she saw my mother.

Mom rushed up to her. Fusa's family stopped walking.

"Here, these are for you. For Christmas. For the ship. You will need them," Mom said.

"Oh, Nelle," Fusa said. She wanted to say more, but I sensed she couldn't.

I had always known my mother's warmth and love because she was my mother, but at this moment, I saw her being a friend. She reached out and pulled Fusa to her. I am not certain Fusa had any choice but to get hugged.

Not much else could happen. Fusa couldn't say, "I'll keep in touch." She didn't know if she could. Mom couldn't say, "Come visit us soon!"

So Fusa thanked my mother and my mother said something about it being a Christmas gift but she didn't even know if Fusa celebrated Christmas. They gave each other a look that made my throat hurt. Then Fusa turned back to her family and walked towards the gate.

Mom stood there for a minute, watching her go. But there were so many other people also heading to the gate that Fusa was soon lost in the crowd.

Dad nudged me. "Take your mother's hand," he whispered.

I slipped my mittened hand into Mom's and she turned and began to walk with me. She didn't say anything. I knew she was praying.

Everywhere Mari and I noted children and adults wearing boots she had purchased on our shopping trips. In a way it made me feel better.

"Dad," Larry said. "I noticed some of the families are stopping in at one of the administration buildings. Do you know what is going on?"

Dad nodded, causing some raindrops to drip onto his shoulders from his hat. "You know a lot of the kids going to Japan are American citizens, but they are too young to stay here without their families. So they are being fingerprinted so they can come back when they are of age."

Larry and I looked at each other. We were both thinking that we would have been in this age group if we had a Japanese family.

A couple of hours passed and we headed back to the barracks. We were thoroughly soaked from the constant rain but at least there we could do something to help. Many of the kids who were not leaving that day came to our quarters to play and Mom baked cookies to send back with them to their families.

Somehow the smell of cookies baking helped.

The next morning we were still asleep when I heard a pounding on the door. My parents both got up and hurried to it. I stayed in bed, listening.

"Why, Yukio!" I heard my mother exclaim. "You're up early!"

"Here, let me help you with that," said Dad. "That is an awfully big bag of potatoes for a little guy like you!"

Mari was awake now and we looked at each other wonderingly.

Yukio was a child who often played at our quarters. In his clear, little-boy voice, he said, "I would like you to French-fry these potatoes, please."

"Well, of course," said my gracious mother, but clearly she was puzzled.

"My mother said maybe you would fry them so we can take French fires with us. Tomorrow we are taking a train to Portland and then a ship to Japan."

Mari looked at me. "Well, let's go start scrubbing potatoes," she said.

The next day, there was another group of people heading to the gates. Among them was a family with a lot of French fried potatoes.

Two days later, on December 29th, my dad said that in all, 3,551 people were now boarding a ship and heading towards Japan.

"I sure wonder what they will find when they get there," Larry said.

"Not food and housing," Mari said.

The new year began without any celebration. It had been almost two weeks since Tomi had told me about Yosh. Her family still hadn't heard anything more from the army.

Other families with an injured son in the army could ask the Red Cross for help. But Tomi's family was in prison. They had no way of contacting the Red Cross or anyone else.

So we just worried and prayed while Tomi's family was going crazy.

When I came in from school, Mari asked if I had heard anything about Yosh, since I had just seen Tomi. I shook my head.

Larry, our eternal optimist, said, "Look at it this way: if Yosh died, the army would tell his family."

Getting myself a glass of milk, I sat down to hope he was right.

"Every day Yosh lives is a day he has survived. That's a definite plus," Larry said, smiling at me.

I wished I could think like he did.

The next time I saw Tomi, she told me that Jiro had decided to sign the loyalty oath and join the army but not until they knew about Yosh. Right now his parents needed him with them as the silent days went by.

While many people were leaving Tule Lake, new ones were arriving. But none of these were internees. I had to do a lot of listening and asking of questions to find out who they were.

Our government has a Department of Justice. I guess you could call them the police of the whole country because their job was to see that laws were followed.

This department sent 15 women and men to Tule Lake. Along with them came a flock of stenographers, who could write or type really fast during court hearings.

I have explained that lots of very discouraged young Japanese-Americans thought they should give up their American citizenship some months back. Since then they decided they had made a big mistake. It was these people that the Department of Justice workers were coming to see.

These hearings were to help decide who would be sent to Japan. Anyone who did not ask for a hearing was told they would be leaving for Japan soon.

Those who asked for hearings were expected to explain why they should not be deported.

My dad was coaching these young people before their hearings.

And apparently, not everyone thought the Department of Justice people would be very helpful. Another group arrived. They were called The Civil Liberties Union. Mom called them "the other side." Their job was to watch out for the rights we have as individuals in the Bill of Rights, which is part of our Constitution.

This was big, big stuff.

While Dad was working, Mom was at the camp hospital, which would close down soon.

Her job was to find places like hospitals and nursing homes for the people who needed that kind of care. The problems were that the elderly people kept changing their minds whether they would stay in the United States or go to Japan.

So Mom would be on the office phones, calling around for places for a person to go in Oregon or California, but also to see if there would be a place on a ship in case they decided to go to Japan instead. She would research which ships might have hospital-type rooms and nurses.

My dear Mom! She was so patient with these confused and hurting people. Often she would work for hours to set up something good for them, only to have them tell her the next day they had changed their minds.

That would have been enough worries for one person, but my mother didn't stop there. She talked with the ambulance drivers and other hospital staff, worrying about what would become of them. Then she started being supportive to the young people waiting for their hearings. There were so many people in one place whose futures were so terribly uncertain.

I could see that this was too much. Mari said so, Larry said so. When Dad was home, he said, "Nelle, you've got to stop taking all this on yourself!"

And of course, she got sick and ended up going to the doctor.

"Helen! Helen!" Tomi was running towards me.

Automatically I glanced up at the guard tower. I have already said those guys paid a lot of attention to anyone running. He was watching us, but he knew me as one of the Hannan kids and he probably had seen Tomi and me meeting each other lots of times. Still, I acted as calm as I could.

Tomi was anything but calm but I could tell she was happy!

"Yosh is alive!!" she shouted. "He is alive!!"

We hugged each other and did a little twirling dance.

She was breathless and I had to wait until she was able to tell me more.

"He was horribly wounded but the army doctors expect him to live. He's lost both legs, but he is alive!" she exclaimed.

I felt a sense of shock go through me, but I knew that all that mattered to his family right now was that he was alive.

In the next few weeks, we learned more. Tomi told me, "Yosh was a big hero. He was wounded because he was saving a lot of other soldiers!"

"Do you know what happened?" I asked.

"Several of the soldiers in his unit were hurt. They had gathered these men together so they could be taken to the aid station. Suddenly, out of nowhere a grenade was thrown–right where they were all lying!

"Yosh saw it first and threw himself on top of it since he knew the others couldn't move. He meant to cover it with his body, but threw himself too far so it was under his legs. This was enough to protect the others with his bulky uniform and gear, and it saved his life too."

"Wow!" I guess that was not the best thing to say, but I was hardly aware that I had even said anything. I was astonished at his bravery.

"He had meant to sacrifice his own life to save the others, but thank heaven that didn't have to happen," Tomi said. "He managed to do it without being killed himself."

She paused then and this time I just stayed quiet.

"He will be getting a medal. It's not the Congressional Medal of Honor but something right below it! It's such an important award that the president awards it personally!"

She went on, "Right now Yosh is being treated on a Navy hospital ship, but when he is well enough, they will ship him to Walter Reed Army Hospital. That is just outside Washington, D.C."

Her eyes were shining with happiness.

I wondered if Tomi and her family would get to leave Tule Lake camp for this ceremony.

So of course I asked my dad.

"Will Tomi and her family go to Washington, D.C. for the ceremony when her brother gets the medal from the president?"

Dad gave me a sad smile. "I doubt that very much, honey. I don't expect they would let her family out for that."

I was stunned. And then I was angry. I wasn't the only one.

Mari said sarcastically, "They probably won't have him go to the White House. How awkward it would be for the government to have a young hero, who gave so much for this country, come to the White House. After all, they can't really explain why his family wasn't with him."

Larry piped up, talking in an exaggerated way as if he were some government official explaining to reporters, "His family? Oh, they couldn't come! We've got them locked up in prison. The whole family, including the grandmother and the baby. We can't trust them."

Larry's acting was funny, but no one laughed. He wasn't trying to make us laugh. Sometimes you just have to use humor to cope when things are really bad.

In the meantime, my own life took a quick and unexpected turn.

"The camp school is closing at the end of the week," I announced to my parents. "We were told that today. So many families have left, there aren't enough students anymore."

I was the only one in the family this affected, as Larry and Mari went to the high school in the town of Tulelake.

"We are enrolling you at Sacred Heart Academy in Klamath Falls," Mom told me a few days later. "You will board there during the week and we will come get you on Fridays so you will be here on the weekends. I don't know how long this will last. Probably only a couple of months, because once the camp is closed, we will be moving on from here too."

I nodded. It was pretty clear that the government was working on closing it. All the people who had said "yes" on the loyalty questionnaire had been released, and of course there had been that huge number of people who had left for Japan late last month.

And I wasn't against this new school idea. It would be good to get out of the camp.

Dad looked at me with a twinkle in his eye. "I have some other news for you too! I have been talking with Alice's father. Their status is still uncertain. They won't be going to Japan, but they won't be allowed to leave the camp yet. I told him about this school and suggested Alice go there too."

I couldn't believe it! I was so excited at first. But I had to ask, "But, Dad, how can Alice's family afford to send her there? If we sleep and eat there, won't it cost a lot of money?"

"That's been taken care of," Dad said lightly. "Well, I am off for another day of hearings. See all of you tonight."

The door closed behind him and I turned to Mom questioningly.

She laughed. She knew I wouldn't let this rest. "Your dad and I decided we would pay for Alice as well as you. Her parents have barely made any money these past four years. I think their income for the whole family is about $19 a month. We can do this. And it will be so good for Alice to have a life outside of the camp. And, Helen, I think you might enjoy it too."

And she was right. The two months Alice and I spent at Sacred Heart Academy were wonderful! The sisters who ran the school welcomed us and we quickly felt at home. Even better, the other girls were delighted to meet us.

It did not take long for everyone to love Alice as I did. No one ever made an anti-Japanese remark to her. Though she was the only Japanese girl at the school at a time when prejudice was so high, it never seemed to occur to the other girls to see Alice as anything but Alice. Funny, creative, sweet Alice!

What a change for her from the past several years!

At night we shared a large room with other girls, but our beds were next to each other. Often we talked quietly before we went to sleep.

After the second week, Alice said in a low voice, "I am so happy here! I love art class and math and English. The sisters are so kind and interested in how we learn! And oh, how I love the food! And, Helen, there are no barbed wire fences here. And no guards. And did I mention how I love the food?"

I smiled in the dark, unaware of Alice's mischief. "And one more thing I love," she whispered. "Pillow fights!"

And wham! Her pillow came flying at me!

I was back in camp that weekend, so of course, Tomi was invited to our quarters.

I missed her during the week. As she would be moving from camp within a few months, her parents decided she could just go without school for now. I think that her mother couldn't bear having Tomi gone from her. So the boarding school was never considered for her.

Today she was clearly excited when she walked in, and we quickly headed to the bedroom. I just looked at her, sensing she had news to share.

Tomi's eyes were shining as she told me, "Yosh is coming home!"

I threw my arms around her and exclaimed how happy I was for her.

And I was delighted, but confused. Home? Did this mean that her family was being released so they could take Yosh to a place where they could care for him?

She saw my confusion. "He's coming here, Helen. To Tule Lake. He can be released from the hospital soon but he will need lots of help and he has so much more healing to do. He needs his family now."

Of course he did. And I was glad, so very, very glad that Yosh had survived and would once again be with his family. It was so good to see Tomi happy.

I did not say, 'How can you care for him in a place like this?' I did not ask if they had a wheelchair or any other equipment Yosh would need. I did not point out that the hospital was closing and the medical people would be leaving soon.

So I was a little surprised when my mouth blurted out, "What about his medal?"

"Oh, we think he received it. We will know more soon. We will know all about what happened to him when he gets here!" she said happily. "I think maybe a general or someone came to the hospital and pinned the medal on him there."

Later I talked to my parents about my confused feelings.

"Tomi is just so relieved they haven't lost Yosh. I doubt she has begun to think about how hard life will be for him and for them to care for him," Mom said.

"But the medal! I know it is just a medal, but he should have gotten it in a big ceremony! I think they pinned it on his pajamas!" I said, rather stubbornly.

"Of course he should have received this in a very honorable way," Mom said. "But I suppose the family has moved on from the issue of how he got his medal or anger that he was not given the honor he deserves. Tomi and her family were blessed with forgiving natures."

Dad added, "This family will have many challenges ahead of them, but they are remarkable. They managed to handle the gross injustice they suffered at the hands of the government, the same government he very nearly died for. I feel we are privileged to know them."

It was February and things were moving fast in the camp now. The hearings led to many decisions, good and bad. During that month, 4,406 of the internees from Tule Lake left for Japan.

Larry was filling me in on the details. "Here is how that

number breaks down: 1,116 of the people headed for Japan were ones who gave up their citizenships."

I cringed, knowing that many were regretting that.

"1,523 were aliens."

People who came from Japan as immigrants to the United States and were never allowed to become citizens.

"And 1,767 are United States citizens," he added.

"That group is mainly children and teens who had to go with their families," I said.

Larry nodded. "We can only wonder what it will be like for them. After years of war, Japan is probably in really bad shape."

"And what is happening with those still here?" I asked.

"According to Dad, there are over 3,000 still waiting for hearings.

That evening our father came home. "I have good news and bad news. Soon a large number of people will be released. None of them will be deported nor sent to the Crystal City center. However, among this group are some who gave up their citizenships, which they haven't gotten back yet. So life will be still be hard for them."

That was indeed mixed news.

It was mixed for me too. Among the 2,737 people leaving were both Alice's and Tomi's families.

Tomi's family needed to find a place to stay, and then Yosh would join them there.

I was so glad they would be leaving this prison. Yet I knew they faced very uncertain futures. And I would miss them.

Though I knew my own time here was ending soon, it was very, very hard saying good-bye.

We promised each other we would keep in touch.

As I stood there, waving and smiling and crying as they passed through those horrible gates, I knew somehow, that we would stay friends.

March 20, 1946. Every single remaining internee was leaving that day.

This imprisonment of innocent people had been a crazy, nightmare-like experience. The last day was to be no different.

Yes, everyone was to leave, but...

Some were being released, with very little money.

They might have homes to go to, but what they may find in those houses was uncertain. Would others have moved in and now refuse to move out? Would any of their possessions still be there? Might their houses been vandalized?

Others of the released group would be looking for shelter because they no longer had homes to go to. Many religious groups had worked to set up places to help. So the people who went to the shelters would no longer be imprisoned, and they would have a safe place to sleep, but it would only be temporary.

Would any of these people find jobs? Would they find acceptance? Would the anti-Japanese feelings just keep on going, keeping them from living comfortable lives?

And yet, they were the lucky ones.

Others were being sent to a Justice Department detention camp in Crystal City, Texas. In other words, they were on their way to yet another prison.

And there was a third group: those who didn't know, on this very last day, if they would be freed or sent to Crystal City!

Feelings, both happy and sad, were running high. And right along with these feelings was fear.

Many came to Mom. Those going into the Texas camp asked her for help with their money. They could not take it with them into Crystal City Center, so they asked if Mom would take the money and send it to relatives who were free now. Mom was careful to keep records of names, amounts and addresses.

Doors were slamming. People were calling to each other. Children cried. Suitcases were piling up.

Every little while, a new list of people who were to be freed would be posted on a bulletin board, so those who did not know their fate were checking that often. There was a regular flow of people running to and from that bulletin board.

Shouts of "I'm free! I'm free!" came from the area as someone read his or her name on the list. It would be a joyful face that turned to run back to pack.

I thought about the people who knew they were headed to the center in Texas. How did they feel each time someone else gained their freedom?

No matter where they were going, everyone had to go to the processing office. Dad was working there that day.

The weather was giving us what March is famous for: wind. It was no a spring-like breeze, but a very cold, persistent and penetrating breeze.

The lines to the processing office were so long, people had to wait outside. They were huddled in their coats, talking and trying to keep the little kids warm. Babies were bundled into blankets.

I had been heartbroken when Alice and Tomi had left. Now it was Mari's turn to grieve.

She was taking care of her friend's toddler, Shigemi. As her mother packed and did all the things that still needed to be done, little Shigemi rode on Mari's hip as Mari ran errands for anyone who needed her help.

"I want to cry and sing at the same time," Mari told me. She was making sandwiches at our house as Shigemi's mother had missed the last meal in the mess hall. "It is such a day of mixed situations. I am crying with some friends, and celebrating for others. I am feeling pretty crazy."

She helped Shigemi finish her milk and bread. "We have to go find your mommy now," Mari said with a cheerfulness I knew she didn't feel.

She buttoned up the little girl's coat and tied on her hand-knitted cap. Then Mari stood up and looked at me. "Her only experience of life is that of a prison."

Mari hastily wiped away a few tears, took Shigemi's tiny, mittened hand and they headed to the door.

I watched them from the window. Shegemi's family was headed to Crystal City. I knew Mari would find a way to stay with them until they passed through the gates.

I had read about ghost towns in stories. I was in one now. This camp had once held thousands of people. Now, there were only a few workers, like my dad, finishing up paper work.

The school building was silent. The hospital was empty. No sounds of pans banging were heard from the mess hall. The church barracks held nothing holy anymore.

I walked towards the internees' barracks. Now they were just hundreds of flimsy buildings, spaces that had so badly housed people who had lost so much.

Standing in one of the alleyways between sets of barracks, the wind whipping up sand, I wondered how Alice and Tomi, were doing. I hoped Alice's grandmother was comfortable now.

I hoped Jiro was all right in the army, and Yosh, whom I never got to meet, was learning how to live without legs.

I imagined Father Hunt on his way to a devastated Japan. I hoped it was warmer there, so he would no longer have to wear that shabby coat!

My foot struck something small so I looked down. There were a few shells, left there by some children who had had no toys.

There was a strange loneliness to the place now. Would people who hadn't come here like I did ever know about the people who were forced to live in these conditions?

Suddenly an idea popped into my head.

Then I ran back to our quarters to begin a project.

The other members of my family were so busy in those final

days before we left Tule Lake that they did not seem to be aware of where I spent much of my time.

One day, I walked out of the bedroom to the kitchen where Mom and Mari were talking.

"There! I'm finished," I announced. "I've been under that bed every afternoon for the past two weeks, and I'm finally done."

They looked at me with mild curiosity. They were also a little amused.

"What have you been doing under the bed for two weeks, dear?" Mom asked.

"Clearly not dusting, from the look of your sweater," Mari joked.

"I've been writing this." I held up a school notebook, waving it like a banner.

"People have to know what happened and I don't think they ever will, unless somebody here and now writes all about this whole crazy thing. Even if it's only in my school tablets with my awful penmanship."

Mom and Mari looked blankly at me. They were listening, but they weren't understanding.

I was feeling very passionate now, so I just kept talking, hoping they would catch on.

"The way all these good and innocent people were imprisoned for four years! The government is going to try to sweep it under the rug if it can. The government knows now how wrong it was and I bet it will keep it a secret unless others talk about it."

"Helen, are you saying you wrote about the situations in these centers?" Mom asked.

I nodded but kept talking. "I know that the grown-ups who worked here, like Dad, can't tell others about it right now if they have to go on working for the government. Telling the world about this would destroy anyone's career if he tried to publish it now."

My mother was standing there, really intrigued but she remained quiet so I could go on.

"I'm young, but I'm old enough to understand what happened here and to write it down. I certainly can't publish it now, probably not for a long, long time. It may be years from now and I may be a little old grandmother by then, but someday our country may be in a situation like this again where they want to lock up thousands of perfectly innocent and harmless people just because they don't look like the rest of us and I'm going to take this out of my little green trunk and fling it to the world. I hope that at least some people will read it and take it to heart so we don't make this same terrible mistake again."

I had run out of steam. My secret was out, my notebook was on the table and I was ready to sit down.

Mari picked up the notebook and came over to sit down next to me on the floor. "May I look at it?" she asked.

I nodded.

She read a couple of pages in silence. A strange expression came over her face.

"Hey, this is good," she said. "I didn't know you could write."

She looked at me with a look that could almost be called respect.

I mentioned before that I saw my sister as the strong and brave "Joan of Arc." I was always awestruck by her. I was the little sister who followed her around like a puppy. And now, she was reading my work, clearly impressed. It was almost more than I could take in.

"I didn't know I could write either, but I felt that I had to try to tell the story and once I started, it just came pouring out. I couldn't have stopped it if I'd tried. It was like something boiling up inside of me, and I had to let it out."

Now Mom took the notebook and sat down at the table to read. After a few minutes she said, "Helen, this was a tremendous idea. The world does need to know about this! And I agree, I think it will be kept a secret by many people. I am so glad you wrote all of it down. I have just begun to read it, but it already looks wonderful!"

Mari nodded. "It is important," she said.

From that day on there was a subtle change in our relationship. My sister and I became equals.

I was no longer the "lil sis." She began calling me "Sis," a person in my own right, not just someone trailing in her wake.

I can tell you it is a very good feeling.

It was mid-April and there was a new warmth in the air now. We Hannans were back in our big old car, and we passed through the gates for the last time.

We were all quiet.

The long war was over but the world was still filled with troubles. Probably the world would always be troubled. But somehow, good is always there too.

I remembered a few years ago when my little cousin Michael was visiting us. Mom was peeling a banana for him. She had her doubts about that banana and warned him, "Be prepared, it may be bad."

Mike looked up at her and grinned. "Aunty Nelle, be prepared it will be good."

And it was.

I felt as if God was whispering, "Trust Me, it will be good."

EPILOGUE

Now it is 2019 and I am a little, old grandmother. The words I wrote in that notebook are finally being published after all these years.

Who would have thought it! It shows you should never give up on your hopes and dreams. They do come true even if it takes 73 years!

□ □ □ PHOTOS □ □ □

Memorial service held at Tule Lake segregation, or isolation, center: imprisoned families mourning their sons who were killed fighting the war. Their military outfit was the 442 Regimental Combat Team composed only of Japanese Americans. It was the most decorated unit in the US Army during WWII.

Helen's father, L.J. Hannan, in uniform

Mari

Helen and her mother in the center, Larry and Mari on the right, with a friend on the left.

Helen's mother, Nelle Hannan, in their quarters

Larry, Helen and Mari at the The Hannans' quarters at Tule Lake.

Mari Hannan

The Hannans were preparing to leave Tule Lake center. Mari is packing and to her right is a "steamer trunk." In the 19th century, travelers used these large cases when going abroad. The Hannans were still using one in the 1940s.

Little Shigemi and Mari.

Little girl playing in bleak surroundings.

*Inside the Hannan's quarters,
where children were often invited to
play. Helen and her mother are in
the background.*

*A little boy out playing, without
any toys.*

This child was born in the Tule Lake center.

This child's was fortunate to have a toy horse, thanks to his grandfather's carpentry skills with scrap lumber. Most children played with trash, sticks and dirt.

Girls Drill Team

Tule Lake school taught by whites hired from outside.

With few materials and tools at first, adults found ways to create some sense of normalcy and fun for everyone, especially the children. One way was to teach aspects of the Japanese culture through dance.

Scenes from the process each person had to go through on the last day.
ABOVE RIGHT: *The scene inside of a truck, which would take people going to the "stockade." As they were going to further imprisonment, they would soon be boarding a train for Texas. On the right is the edge of Mari's face. She was able to board this truck because she was carrying a friend's baby and the guards didn't recognize her. She decided she wanted to remain with these friends as long as possible, as they were not to be freed.*

On the last day at Tule Lake center, women and babies waited inside the processing station. Big cardboard tags were stapled to their good wool coats, with an ID number and information showing where they were being sent. Helen noted that it reminded her of how the Nazis tattooed prisoners. "The whole thing was completely dehumanizing. But you can see their dignity through it all."

Scenes of the day Tule Lake center closed. Despite the difficult circumstances, people dressed formally.

Days before the center was to close, the young people had gotten permission to have a farewell dance as families would soon be going separate ways. They had decorated the gym, but the afternoon of the dance, the gym was mysteriously burned down, ending the fun. The silhouettes in the photos are the young people watching it burn.

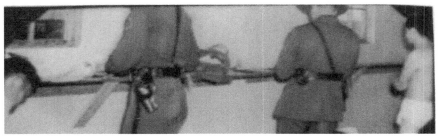

There was still more indignity for some people on the last day. Prisoners who were to get on a train for further imprisonment had to strip down to their underwear to be searched by armed guards.

When Tule Lake Segregation Center was closing, some people were still considered dangerous. They were sent by train to further imprisonment in Crystal City Texas.

Two days to prepare, and only one suitcase to bring—to where?
This family did not know when this picture was taken.

Mari, Helen and friends.

*Tule Lake Segregation Center. Barbed wire around barren grounds,
and towers with guards and guns.*

APPENDIX

The world has changed a great deal since Helen was a child. Here is some information about that time to help you better understand her story.

- THE UNITED STATES DURING HELEN'S CHILDHOOD
- A LITTLE ABOUT THE WAR AND ITS AFFECTS ON THE WORLD
- A STORY OF RACISM: WHY WERE INNOCENT JAPANESE-AMERICANS IMPRISONED?
- SOME WHO HELPED
- WHAT HAPPENED AFTER THE WAR?
- TRYING TO LEARN FROM THE PAST

THE UNITED STATES DURING HELEN'S CHILDHOOD

Between World War I and World War II, there was the Great Depression.

Helen was born in 1933. The whole world was in the Great Depression during that time.

A depression is a time when a country has serious money problems. These problems are connected to each other. For example, if people have less money, they don't buy as many things. Factories that make those things sell less, so the workers there lose their jobs. Without jobs, those workers may not be able to buy enough food for their families, and may even have to leave their homes.

Something else that can cause money problems is weather. Months of bad weather may mean that farmers can't grow as much food. This affects the farm families, and also people who work in places that prepare the food for stores. With less food to prepare, there is less work. Workers there may be told to leave their jobs. There is less food for stores to sell, so store workers may lose their jobs. Stores owners may have to give up their stores.

During a depression, banks often close down before people can get their money. Without money, people can't keep paying for their homes. Hundreds of thousands of families were forced to leave their homes during the Great Depression. Some moved in with relatives, but some families ended up sleeping outside and asking others for food.

The Great Depression started in 1929 and lasted ten years! It started in the United States and then affected many other countries too. It was truly terrible for millions of people.

Helen's family did not lose their home, but like everyone else, they had to be very careful how they used their money. In this story, Helen mentions the many hungry men who came to their house. They had left families to travel, in hopes of finding jobs. She speaks of neighborhood children who had less to eat than she did. Her mother somehow managed to feed not only her family, but also some of those hungry travelers and neighbor children.

Many of the causes of the Great Depression were blamed on the president, Herbert Hoover. Before Helen was born, Franklin Delano Roosevelt became president, replacing Hoover. Roosevelt was able to bring about laws that helped people who were suffering because of the Depression. Helen's parents agreed then he had done much good.

The Great Depression ended about the time World War II started. There are arguments about whether it was the war that ended the Depression or not. However, many young people did go into the army, navy, etc., which meant they now had jobs. And others began working in factories to make bombs and airplanes.

The 1940's were quite different from the 1930's.

IMAGINE THE 1940'S:

- Most, but not all, homes in the United States had electricity.
- Many homes had radios.
- Though television had been invented, very few Americans had television sets.

- To learn about the events in the world, people mainly read newspapers. Also, short films about the war were shown in theaters before the regular movies.
- Less than 40% of American homes had telephones. Cell phones were not in use for another 50 years. No one in the 1940's would have ever heard the term 'cell phone.'
- Most people did not know about computers; it would be 30 more years before computers would be used in offices, and about 40 years before they were used in homes.
- There was nothing at all like the Internet.
- Compared to today, most families owned less clothing and shoes, toys, furniture, cars, etc.
- Families did not go to fast food restaurants. Most had never tasted pizza. Those became popular about ten years after WWII.
- The United States had only 48 states. When Pearl Harbor was bombed in 1941, Hawaii was not a state, but a territory of the United States. It became a territory in1898 and a state (the 50th) in August 1959. (Alaska became the 49th state in January 1959.)

Helen remembers the changes she saw as an eight-year old right after the bombing of Pearl Harbor:

"We became afraid. We had drills, like fire drills at school, but these drills happened at home too: a siren in the neighborhood would sound, and everyone hurried to cover their windows with black curtains and turn off lights. If you were outside, you ran to the nearest house.

"Our factories started making war equipment, using materials that would have been used to make children's shoes, toys, tires or new cars. We saved paper, patched our clothes and shoes, planted big vegetable gardens and listened to the radio for news of the war. "

A LITTLE ABOUT THE WAR
AND ITS AFFECTS ON THE WORLD

World War Two is called that because it was the second time many countries fought each other at the same time. World War One ended only 20 years before World War II began. Many of the countries that fought each other in the first war again fought each other in the second war.

World War I:

The Allies included Britain, France, Russia, Italy and the United States.

The Allies fought against the Central Powers that included Germany, Austria-Hungary, the Ottoman Empire and Bulgaria.

World War II:

The Allies included Britain, France, Soviet Union (USSR), United States, Australia, Belgium, Brazil, Canada, China, Denmark, Greece, Netherlands, New Zealand, Norway, Poland, South Africa and Yugoslavia.

They fought the Axis powers, which were Germany, Japan and Italy.

It is impossible to know exactly how many people died as a result of World War II. There are some estimates:

- Soldiers from both sides: the numbers range from 50 million to more than 80 million.
- Civilians from both sides: 50 to 55 million, which includes 19 to 28 million deaths from war-related disease and famine.

A great deal of research has been done to look at how that war affected the world. Helen wrote about the changes she saw:

"World War II had overwhelming effects on the world that are still felt today. You could almost say a lot of the way that the world is today is the result of WWII.

"The map of Europe changed, as it does after every war. The Eastern half disappeared behind the "Iron Curtain", as it was called. That was the part controlled by the USSR

[Russia and her satellites]. Germany was cut right in half, as was the city of Berlin. The lives of the people in those areas were desperately hard.

"The areas controlled by the western Allies fared better. There was rebuilding of destroyed cites, an attempt to reunite families and to feed people.

"From that time up to the present it was obvious that the U.S. and Russia (U.S.S.R.) were enemies, even if we are not actively shooting at each other. We united just to defeat the common enemy Hitler and for no other reason. Over the years this state of affairs has been known as "The Cold War".

"Another great effect of WWII was the general shaking up of the various cultures of the world. People and nations who had never known one another discovered each other as armies moved around the world.

"People learned that we are all really basically very much alike everywhere. The world "discovered America" as the American army went everywhere and created a lot of good will. America's position of prominence in the world was established politically and militarily.

"One side effect is that the United States' "pop culture" has spread to other parts of the world. This may not have done a great deal of good for people in faraway places.

"WWII changed our American culture as well. The draft brought together young men of very different backgrounds--socially, economically, geographically and educationally. Men from Brooklyn met and befriended men from Oklahoma. Italian-American men from San Francisco fishing families became life-long friends with Irish-American men from Boston. Prejudices were overcome. If someone saved your life yesterday he must be a pretty good person, even if he has a regional accent and makes mistakes in grammar. This brought about a good shaking up of our culture as well, which we still feel today."

A STORY OF RACISM: WHY WERE INNOCENT JAPANESE-AMERICANS IMPRISONED?

Long before World War II, there was great discrimination against Asians in the United States. It began more than one hundred and fifty years before World War II! A timeline will show the building up of the racism that led to the mass imprisonment of innocent people in 1942.

1790: The U.S. Congress passed an act that said only immigrants who were not slaves and were "white" could become citizens.

1873: People of African descent were added to the law so they could become citizens, eight years after slavery was abolished.

1882: Congress passed the Chinese Exclusion Act. No Chinese person could come to the United States after that; this lasted for 60 years.

1885: Owners of sugar cane farms recruited Japanese workers to come to Hawaii to work.

In Wyoming, there are riots and violence against the Chinese people who were there already.

1891: Japanese workers came to the mainland U.S. for work on farms.

1894: The law of 1790 was used to state that no Japanese immigrant could become a citizen of the U.S.

1900-1905: During these years there was a great deal of racism against Japanese people in California.

1906: Schools in San Francisco separated any child of Chinese, Japanese or Korean backgrounds from other children.

1913: Laws were passed so that any immigrant who was not allowed to become a citizen could not buy or rent land.

1920: A time of more racist laws and threats towards Japanese people and now their Japanese-American children. Much of this was because they were successful farmers, so other farmers were angry and perhaps jealous.

1924: Congress passed the Immigration Act of 1924 that stated there could be no more Japanese immigration to the U.S.

1939: World War II began in Europe. President Roosevelt asked for a report about Japanese-Americans, as he was concerned about a possible war with Japan.

November 1941: The report was finished. The U.S. War Department, the U.S. Military and the FBI (also part of the US government) agreed that most Japanese Americans were loyal to the U.S. and did not pose a threat to national security.

December 7, 1941: Japan bombed U.S. ships and planes at the Pearl Harbor military base in Hawaii.

Immediately, the FBI began arresting Japanese immigrants identified as community leaders. Among these were religious leaders, Japanese language teachers, newspaper publishers, and heads of organizations. Within 48 hours, 1,291 people, mainly men, were arrested. Most of them were jailed for the rest of the war, separated from their families, even though the report said these people were not dangerous. How could these arrests happen so quickly? The FBI had been making a list for some time, ready to arrest them.

December 8, 1941: War was declared against Japan by the President and passed by Congress.

Executive order 9066:

Immediately after the bombing of Pearl Harbor, most Americans had feelings of great fear, confusion and anger.

Officials in the federal government and in the military began pressuring President Roosevelt to imprison tens of thousands of Japanese-Americans and Japanese immigrants who were not allowed to become citizens.

Many of the people encouraging the president knew they had much to gain from this. They acted out of greed and hatred, not fear or caution.

In February, just ten weeks after the Japanese bombed Pearl Harbor and the United States had gone to war with Japan, President Roosevelt signed Executive Order 9066.

This gave the military far-reaching powers. They could ban any citizen from a sixty-mile wide area on the West Coast. This included parts of Washington, Oregon, California and southern Arizona.

Some Japanese people had already been arrested and put into prison. Some others were able to leave the West Coast quickly but most did not have a place to go. With Order 9066, the forced relocation began.

By June, just four months after the signing of 9066, between 110,000—120,000 Japanese-Americans were imprisoned in what were called "internment camps.

And who were these imprisoned people?

Anyone who was at least 1/16th Japanese was evacuated. That means if a child had one great-great grandparent who had been Japanese, that child was to be imprisoned. Mostly likely that great-great-grandparent had been born at least 100 years before the child was born!

About 17,000 of the children who were imprisoned were under the age of 10. Many were babies. Babies were born in the camps, too.

Along with all the children, these people were also imprisoned: teens, parents, grandparents, single people, people with handicaps, people who had sicknesses, doctors, farmers, teachers, coaches, nurses, artists, business owners, religious leaders, writers and many others.

In addition to loosing their homes, jobs, and several years of their lives, some of these prisoners were marked as people to be used for a prisoner of war exchange.

The United States was at war with Germany and Italy too. Were any German-Americans or Italian-Americans imprisoned?

Order 9066 also applied to some other Americans, those of Italian or German descent. Like the Japanese-Americans, they were being watched and some were imprisoned immediately. They suffered in similar ways as the Japanese-Americans, and some of them, too, were used for prisoner exchanges at the end of the war.

However, there was one huge difference: the numbers of innocent people imprisoned.

People with Italian background:
- 3,200 resident aliens were arrested.
- More than 300 of them were imprisoned in centers.

People with German background:
- About 11,000 German residents, some who had become US citizens, were arrested.
- More than 5000 were imprisoned in centers.

People with Japanese background:
- Between 110,000 and 120,000 were sent to relocation centers (also called "internment camps.")

How many of these "camps" existed and where were they?

There were several kinds of centers, most often called "camps." Helen found this term distressingly incorrect. She felt the word "camp" sounded like a fun place and she knew first-hand that fun did not describe Amache or Tule Lake Centers.

The main kinds of centers were 1) temporary detention centers, 2) relocation centers and 3) Justice Department centers.

TEMPORARY DETENTION CENTERS

As the relocation centers were being hastily built, thousands of people had already been forced to leave their homes. They were sent to temporary detention centers. Some of these places were set up in fairgrounds or racetracks. Some families had to live and sleep in horse stalls.
- Fresno, California
- Manzanar, California (this site later became a relocation center)
- Marysville, California
- Mayer, Arizona
- Merced, California
- Pinedale, California

- Pomona, California
- Portland, Oregon
- Puyallup, Washington
- Sacramento, California
- Salinas, California
- Santa Anita, California
- Stockton, California
- Tanforan, San Bruno, California
- Tulare, California
- Turlock, Byron, California

These were used from late March 1942 until mid-October, 1942. By then, the people in these centers were moved to the relocation centers.

RELOCATION CENTERS (or Permanent Detention Camps)
- Topaz Internment Camp, Central Utah
- Colorado River or Poston Internment Camp, Arizona
- Gila River Internment Camp, Phoenix, Arizona
- Granada or Amache Internment Camp, Colorado
- Heart Mountain Internment Camp, Wyoming
- Jerome Internment Camp, Arkansas
- Manzanar Internment Camp, California
- Minidoka Internment Camp, Idaho
- Rohwer Internment Camp, Arkansas
- Tule Lake Internment Camp, California; this became a segregation center in 1943

JUSTICE DEPARTMENT INTERNMENT CENTERS

U.S. Department of Justice Centers were used to imprison people who were considered the "most dangerous" people. These included families with children.

Some of these people had never even lived in the United States! The U.S. government removed 2,200 people of Japanese descent living in Latin and South America from their countries!

They were then placed into the Justice Department camps, mainly in Crystal City, Texas.

About 1,800 were from Peru. The other 250 people arrived from Panama, Bolivia, Colombia, Costa Rica, Cuba, Ecuador, El Salvador, Mexico, Nicaragua, and Venezuela.

Imprisoned in Crystal City were also German-American families.

Many of the people at Crystal Lake were considered "suspicious" but were also seen as candidates for prisoner exchange programs at the end of the war. Some of these people were sent to Japan or Germany. Many were children and had never lived in these countries before. Among these people were many with American citizenship.

- Santa Fe, NM
- Bismarck, ND
- Crystal City, TX
- Missoula, MT
- Seagoville, Texas
- Kooskia, Idaho

SOME WHO HELPED

This story tells of the many ways the Hannan family helped those who were treated so unjustly.

Many Americans, especially those who did not live near the West Coast, were totally unaware of the imprisonment of Japanese-Americans and immigrants. Helen's father only found out because of his work in the army.

There were Americans who knew but didn't care, or were relieved because of their attitudes towards others who seemed different from them.

And then there were those who, like Helen's family, decided to do something about this. They found a variety of ways: through their jobs, religions, protests and politics. Here are just a few examples:

JOBS:

- Clara Breed: As a young librarian in San Diego, Clara Breed had befriended many middle-and high school-aged students who were Japanese-Americans. When the forced incarceration was announced, she realized that many of "her" young readers would be leaving San Diego for harsher places. They had been happy and enthusiastic learners, but she saw a change in them as they were preparing to leave. Worried, her response was to give them self-addressed, stamped postcards and asked them to let her know how she could contact them. During the course of this imprisonment, she wrote to them and sent books, magazines and small items they needed, like toothbrushes and soap. Most importantly, she was a connection with their former lives and a good friend. It was not a quick or easy thing for her to do, with war rationing and a limited personal budget. She was even able to visit some of the centers a few times.

  She also wrote to many members of Congress and published articles protesting the imprisonment. She worked, again through letters, to get college-aged students in the centers to be allowed to attend schools in the Midwest, and to reunite families where the father had been imprisoned apart from the rest of his family.

  Clara Breed maintained friendships with the people she had helped for the rest of her life.

- Bob Fletcher: Bob Fletcher was young man who worked as a State Agricultural Inspector in California. Through his work, he knew many farmers, including some who would soon be forced into relocation centers.

  "I did know a few of them (Japanese-American farmers) pretty well and never did agree with the evacuation," he said years later. "They were the same as anybody else. It was obvious they had nothing to do with Pearl Harbor."

One of these farmers asked Bob to take care of his farm for however long the imprisonment would last. Even though he already had a job and his own farm, Bob agreed. Soon he also consented to take care of two more farms. He had to learn how to grow the crops the Japanese-Americans farmers grew. And he quit his job to care for four farms.

Some of his non-Japanese neighbors who were farmers resented Bob for this.

But that did not bother him. For the three years he farmed a total of 90 acres, working 16-hour days. Bob's wife, Teresa, helped him. They lived in the bunkhouse of one farm, feeling they did not want to disturb any of the families' homes by living in them.

Though the farmers had offered Bob all the profits from their farms while they were imprisoned, Bob spilt the money equally for each family. They returned to their farms and homes, which were unharmed, and they even had money in the bank.

· Wayne Collins: A San Francisco civil liberties attorney, Wayne Collins defended Fred Korematsu (see Protest section) and lost. After that, he worked to close down the stockade (or the prison-within-a-prison) at Tule Lake.

From 1944-45, about 3000 Japanese immigrants and citizens were to be sent to Japan after giving up their American citizenships. Wayne brought four huge cases to the U.S. District Court of San Francisco. He was able to get a court order just days before a ship was to leave for Japan with Japanese people. This order said they could not be deported until their cases could be heard before a judge. Collins argued that those who gave up their citizenship did so because of the "pressure-cooker environment" of Tule Lake and influence from the Hoshidan.

The court said that each case should be evaluated individually—every single person would have to state in court that they had been influenced, or coerced, into giving up their citizenship.

Starting in 1951 and continuing until 1968, Wayne Collins worked on this. He restored the citizenship of 4,987 Americans! He also worked to prevent hundreds of Japanese-Peruvians, who had been forced to come to centers in the United States, from being sent to Japan.

RELIGION:

· The Colorado Council of Churches: This group published "The Japanese in Our Midst." This booklet helped readers understand what was truthful and what was not truthful about the people forced to live in the relocation centers.

Some members from the Rocky Mountain Region and the Denver areas also publicly and privately supported the evacuees.

· The American Friends Service Committee (AFSC): This group, also called the Quakers, worked in many ways to be of help. One way was through a program to get young people out of the relocation centers and into colleges and universities in the Midwest and Eastern states. This program helped students who were already in college or had qualified to start college.

Another program helped other young people get jobs near colleges so they could work until they could apply and start school.

Hundreds of others received help through the hostels set up by the AFSC in many American cities. Theses hostels were opened for Japanese-Americans leaving the relocation centers at the end of the war. Many did not have homes and jobs to return to. This gave them places to stay while looking for work. Once they had jobs, they got help from the AFSC to find homes for themselves and their families.

• American Baptist Home Mission Society: Many churches in the United States sympathized with the Japanese-Americans, but most failed to create significant protests in the brief time in which they could have caused change. Later, however, they found a variety of ways to help. The American Baptist Home Mission Society published a pamphlet, which offered positive attitudes towards Japanese-Americans in hopes of encouraging acceptance and open-mindedness.

To see parts of the pamphlet: http://www.slate.com/blogs/the_vault/2015/11/09/protests_against_internment_camps_during_world_war_ii.html

• Maryknoll: This is a Catholic mission movement that has served in many places in the world since 1911. It includes sisters, priests and brothers, lay missioners and affiliates.

In addition to those mentioned in the story, Fathers John F. Swift and Joseph A. Hunt, there were other Maryknoll missioners who served imprisoned Japanese-Americans is at least eight of the centers, in a great variety of ways. Here are a few examples:

Sisters Bernadette Yoshimochi and Susanna Hayashi were Maryknoll Sisters who were both of Japanese descent. They were working on the West Coast when the United States entered the war. They could have left the militarized area to live at Maryknoll headquarters in New York, but instead choose to be imprisoned with thousands of others. They lived and worked in the relocation center called Manzanar.

Father Leo J. Steinbeck also served in Manzanar. He was in Japan in the earlier part of the war and was imprisoned there. He chose to go to Manzanar when he was able to return to the United States. He was not allowed to live within the center, so lived in a nearby town and came to the center each day.

This team encouraged the organization of numerous clubs for various age groups and interests as well choirs.

They taught religion classes and prepared families for baptisms, etc. Like Fathers Swift and Hunt, Father Steinbeck also shopped for the internees.

Sister Yae Ono was not a Maryknoll Sister while she was in a relocation center. As a child she attended the Methodist Church, and chose to be baptized a Catholic in a Maryknoll church in Los Angeles when she was 24. Later that same year, she was incarcerated at Manzanar Relocation Center. Along with her sister, Minnie, Yae assisted Sisters Bernadette Yoshimochi and Susanna Hayashi and Father Leo Steinbeck. Like Mari, she taught children religion classes. She decided she wanted to enter Maryknoll to become a sister during that time. It was after great difficulty that she was able to leave Manzanar in 1944 to go to New York and begin her studies.

Father Leopold Tibesar seved in Minidoka Relocation Center. He was able to get students and some families to Chicago for school with the help of his brother, Franciscan Father Serephin Tibesar. When Minidoka closed, Father Leopold went to Chicago to help settle internees in the Chicago area and then went to work in Japan.

Father Hugh Lavery and others tried to intercede on the part of orphaned children cared for by Maryknoll Sisters, and also tried to find places for large groups from their churches to move to, out of the militarized zone. When they couldn't do that, they found many other smaller ways to make things a little easier.

PROTEST:

• Gordon Hirabayashi: Gordon was a college student in the state of Washington when the United States entered World War II. Just after the entry into the war, a curfew was put on anyone of Japanese descent. They had to be home by 8 p.m. He ignored the curfew. When others went into relocation centers, he refused. He said the government's actions were racial discrimination. He was jailed in different prisons over the next few years for these acts and also for refusing to go into the military. He believed the loyalty questionnaire was unfair because it was racially discriminatory. He spent nearly two years in prisons. He took his case to the Supreme Court and lost.

"When my case was before the Supreme Court in 1943, I fully expected that as a citizen the Constitution would protect me," Mr. Hirabayashi.

"Surprisingly, even though I lost, I did not abandon my beliefs and my values," he said. "And I never look at my case as just my own, or just as a Japanese-American case. It is an American case, with principles that affect the fundamental human rights of all Americans."

Mr. Hirabayashi graduated from the University of Washington and became a sociology professor, teaching at the American University of Beirut, the American University in Cairo and in Canada at the University of Alberta in Edmonton, where he lived.

Forty years passed before the United States government declared that he had done nothing wrong.

· Minoru Yasui and Fred Korematsu also chose to fight the curfew and incarceration of Japanese-Americans. Like Gordon Hirabayashi, they suffered jail time, took their cases to the Supreme Court and lost and were finally vindicated forty years later.

· Milton S. Eisenhower:

This man spent his life working for the good of many people in a variety of places and ways. He worked for the U.S Department of Agriculture, served as president of three important universities where he was able to build up these schools, and he was an advisor to three United States presidents!

During World War II, he was also appointed director of the War Relocation Authority. He was against the mass imprisonment. He came up with several plans to make this much easier on the Japanese–Americans, such as letting them work outside of the camps, and getting protections for the homes, lands and businesses they were forced to leave behind. But he met with so much resistance, he could do very little. Discouraged, he resigned from the WRA after only three months. He said he was leaving the job in protest in what he saw as incarcerating innocent citizens.

POLITICS:

• Ralph L. Carr: As the war was ending, the governor of Colorado, Ralph Carr, welcomed people who had been interned in the relocation centers to settle in his state.

He said, "This is a difficult time for all Japanese-speaking people. We must work together for the preservation of our American system and the continuation of our theory of universal brotherhood . . . If we do not extend humanity's kindness and understanding to [the Japanese-Americans], if we deny them the protection of the Bill of Rights, if we say that they must be denied the privilege of living in any of the 48 states without hearing or charge of misconduct, then we are tearing down the whole American system."

But among other governors and public figures, anti-Japanese feelings were running very high. Carr was quite alone in his beliefs. Because of his accepting and welcoming attitude, he was easily defeated when he ran for Senate later. He retired from public life after that.

However, his support for the Japanese-Americans and the courage it took to work for their rights is still remembered. Just outside the Colorado's governor's office is a plaque that says, "Dedicated to Governor Ralph L. Carr: a wise, humane man, not influenced by the hysteria and bigotry directed against the Japanese-Americans during World War II. By his humanitarian efforts no Colorado resident of Japanese ancestry was deprived of his basic freedoms, and when no others would accept the evacuated West Coast

Japanese except for confinement in internment camps, Governor Carr opened the doors and welcomed them to Colorado. The spirit of his deeds will live in the hearts of true Americans."

WHAT HAPPENED AFTER THE WAR?

THE HANNAN FAMILY:

After Tule Lake Segregation Center closed on March 20, 1946, the Hannans stayed on until Helen's father, Lawrence, had finished his work there. The family moved to Sacramento, California, where Lawrence began a new job.

None of the Hannan family went back to Chicago. They settled in California and the family, including descendants, has been there ever since.

Helen recalls that for years after their experiences in the centers, people who had been imprisoned there, came to the Hannan home with fruit, flowers and vegetables. They were, Helen said, "so grateful for the things that he (her father) had done for them in camp."

Lawrence Hannan: His work in Sacramento, California, was for the U.S. government program called the Bureau of Reclamation. This organization works to manage, develop and protect major sources of water.

He continued working for justice for the rest of his life. Just before his death in 1964, he was assisting a Native American whose land had been falsely claimed by others.

Nelle Hannan: After the death of her husband, Nelle continued to live in their house by herself. She gardened, with a special interest in roses, and volunteered for a hospital auxiliary. When health issues caused her to use a wheelchair, she moved in with Helen and her young family. She continued to help with family chores, including gardening, saying "I still have my eyes, hands and brain." Helen says her mother was amazing, and "was one of a kind to the end." Nelle died in 1971.

Mari Hannan: When her family moved to Sacramento, Mari soon reconnected with several of her girl friends she had met in the centers. She found that they were working in low-paying jobs. Convinced they had settled for this work because they now had fears as a result of their unjust imprisonment, Mari persuaded them to have the courage to seek better employment—and they all got better jobs! While still in her teens, Mari corresponded often with U.S. Attorney General Tom Clark, urging him to restore the citizenships of many Japanese-Americans and stop deporting them.

She married Robert Brennan and they had ten children. In the 1970's, she went back to school and became an obstetrical nurse. She died in 1986.

Larry Hannan: Larry fulfilled his dream of going to law school and become a lawyer. He married Sharon Braden and they had four children, one boy and three girls

Helen Hannan: Like her father, Helen graduated from Creighton University. She married Gilbert Parra and they had four sons and one daughter. After their family was grown, Helen spent 20 years as a volunteer for the Sacramento Food Bank and Family Services where she was instrumental in establishing a Parent Education program and a children's clothes closet. She is retired now and enjoys her large and close family and gardening.

THOSE WHO WERE SENT TO JAPAN:

This is the number of people who were deported to Japan when Tule Lake Segregation Center closed:

1523 Issei (first generation to emigrate to the U.S. from Japan)

1116 Nisei (second generation, born in the U.S., many of whom had who given up their citizenships

1718 minor children

WHAT MANY OF THESE PEOPLE EXPERIENCED:
ON THE OCEAN LINER

- Some slept in bunk beds four levels high. These were made of canvas, and held up by chains attached to pipes.
- These beds were in the hold of the ship, so they had to take stairs with no railings at least four levels down from the top of the ship.
- Many people were motion sick during the voyage.
- Many did not have winter coats, so shared thin blankets given to them.
- On one ship, passengers received small Christmas gifts from the American Friends and Service Committee (AFSC).

WHAT MANY OF THEM SAW WHEN THEIR OCEAN LINER ARRIVED AT A PORT IN JAPAN:

- The ocean liner could not come into the port because of the many sunken Japanese ships there in the water.
- Barges were brought in to take people off the ships and to land. Among these arrivals, there were still people from the United States who believed that Japan had won the war! Then people near docks began calling to the passengers, asking if they had food or candy from the United States. These conversations between Japanese living in Japan and the arrivals led the arrivals to realize that Japan had lost the war. For many, they had to face the fact that they had brought their children and grandchildren to a country that was now in a terrible situation.

ON TO EVACUATION CAMPS:

- From the barges, the arrivals from the United States were taken to makeshift camps. The food and supplies were very minimal. People were hungry and cold.
- There they gathered into groups, depending on where they were going. Some were going to where they hoped they had relatives. Others went to areas where they hoped to find work.

SETTING OFF:

- Once they left the evacuation camps, the arrivals from the United States all saw much destruction and suffering caused by the war. They took trains that had broken windows. At times, they encountered sections of the train tracks had been destroyed by bombs. The passengers, already cold, tired and hungry, would have to walk.
- Along the way they saw sick and homeless people sleeping in train stations if the stations still had roofs.
- Some saw acres of farmland that had been burned.
- Those going to Hiroshima and Nagasaki found huge parts of those cities completely destroyed and many badly injured people.
- In other areas, the arrivals may have found their relatives, but parts of their homes were destroyed or the relatives had so little food it was difficult for them to take the new family in. People worked together to find ways to pay for what little food was available.
- Many of the young adults found jobs because they spoke and wrote in both English and Japanese. Some of them were able to return to the United States without their parents, to get jobs and go to school.

THOSE WHO WERE SENT TO CRYSTAL CITY:

When Tule Lake Segregation Center closed on March 19, 1946, among those still there were people who had given up their citizenship but wanted to get it back.

Some were not allowed to be free:

- 406 people and their 43 family members were put on a train and shipped to the Department of Justice family internment camp in Crystal City, Texas.
- Most likely those people were deported to Japan

THOSE WHO WERE FREED:

For the "lucky" people who were not sent to Crystal City camp or deported to Japan, there were many situations. Some who went back to their hometowns found their homes intact, but others found theirs vandalized and their possessions gone.

Some had been forced to give up their homes because they could not afford to make payments. They were completely homeless. Many no longer had jobs. Some went to hostels to live until they could find jobs and housing.

Some chose to start their lives over in an area of the West Coast different from where they had lived earlier. Forty-three thousand Japanese Americans left the West Coast to pursue lives elsewhere in America.

Many people never recovered financially. What they had worked for before the war was gone and they were never able to regain what they had. This affected their children and grandchildren. Some suffered emotionally for the rest of their lives, with memories, fears and feeling of loss.

TRYING TO LEARN FROM PAST MISTAKES

In 1981, thirty-six years after World War II ended, the U.S. Congress appointed a committee to study Executive Order 9066 and all that resulted from it. This group published their report in 1982. It was called Personal Justice Denied.

It stated that:
- the decisions leading to the order were shaped by race, prejudice, war hysteria, and failure of political leadership.
- widespread ignorance of Japanese-Americans helped cause this order to be done too quickly, and carried out because of fear and anger at Japan.

It took another six years before the US government acted on these findings. The response came in the form of the Civil Liberties Act, signed by President Ronald Reagan in 1988.

This offered a formal apology and paid out $20,000 in compensation to each surviving victim. Many felt this was a small compensation for what people had lost and suffered. The families of victims who had already died did not receive any money, yet these later generations were affected by their parents' or grandparents' mistreatment.

Today, it is recognized that there were only 10 Americans convicted of spying for Japan during World War II. None of them had any Japanese ancestry.

ONE MORE STORY FROM HELEN:

"I met a man who had a very good, responsible job in Los Angeles. When he heard that I had been at Tule Lake too, he confided that he always had a bad feeling of having been put into prison.

"I told him, 'You were put into prison because the government did something bad to you. You were seventeen years old then! What wrong could you have done? You didn't' do anything bad!'

"He listened and then said with amazement, 'You know, no one has ever told me that—I feel much better now.'"

BIBLIOGRAPHY

BOOKS:

Daniels, Roger. Prisoners Without Trial, Japanese Americans in World War II. Farrar, Straus and Giroux, 1993.

Dempster, Brian Komei, Editor. From Our Side of the Fence, Growing Up in America's Concentration Camps. Produced by Japanese Cultural and Community Center of Northern California, 2001

Gordon, Linda and Gary Y. Okihiro, editors. Impounded, Dorothea Lange and the Censored Images of Japanese American Internment. W.W. Norton and Company, 2006

Harris, Catherine Embree. Dusty Exile, Looking Back At Japanese Relocation During World War II. Mutual Publishing, 1999.

Hirasuna, Delphine. The Art of Gaman, Arts and Crafts from the Japanese American Interment Camps 1942-1946, Ten Speed Press, 2005.

Houston, Jeanne Wakatsuki and James D. Houston. Farewell to Manzanar. Random House, 1973

Inada, Lawson Fusao, Editor. Only What We Could Carry, The Japanese American Internment Experience. Heyday, 2000.

Irvin, Catherine. Twice Orphaned, Voices from the Children's Village of Manzanar. Cener for Oral and Public History, California State University, Fullerton, 2008.

Izumi, Tomo. The Crystal City Story, One Family's Experience with the World War II Japanese Interment Camps. 2016

Kashiwagi, Hiroshi. Swimming in the American, A Memoir and Selected Writings. Asian American Curriculum Project, 2005.

Mochizuki, Ken. Baseball Saved Us. Dom Lee, illustrator; Lee and Low Books, Inc. 1993.

Oppenheim, Joanne. Dear Miss Breed, True Stories of the Japanese American Incarceration During World War II and A Librarian Who Made a Difference. Scholastic, 2006.

Otsuka, Julie. When the Emperor Was Divine. Random House, 2002.

Reeves, Richard. Infamy. Henry Holt and Company, 2015.

Russell, Jan Jarboe. The Train to Crystal City, FDR'S Secret Prisoner Exchange Program and America's Only Family Internment Camp During World War II. Simon and Schuster, 2015.

Seigel, Shizue. In Good Conscience, Supporting Japanese-Americans During the Internment. AACP, Inc. 2006.

Uchida, Yoshiko. The Bracelet. Illustrated by Joanna Yardley; Philomel Books, 1976.

Uchida, Yoshiko. The Invisible Thread. Julian Messner,1991.

Uchida, Yoshiko. Journey Home. Illustrated by Charles Robinson. Aladdin Books, 1978.

Werner, Emmy E. Through the Eyes of Innocents, Children Witness World War II. Westview Press, 2000.

ARTICLES/WEBSITES BY SUBJECT

ART

https://www.npr.org/templates/story/story.
php?storyId=126557553

https://calisphere.org/item/ark:/13030/kt829022xs/

http://www.latimes.com/entertainment/arts/la-ca-cm-eaton-collection-20180105-htmlstory.html

https://densho.org/crafting-beauty-dissent-and-design-in/
DETAINMENT CENER LISTS:

http://www.momomedia.com/CLPEF/camps.html

https://en.wikipedia.org/wiki/Internment_of_Japanese_Americans

HELPERS

Breed, Clara: http://encyclopedia.densho.org/Clara_Breed/

Collins, Wayne: http://encyclopedia.densho.org/Wayne%20M.%20
Collins/

Fletcher, Bob: http://encyclopedia.densho.org/Bob_Fletcher/

Hunt, Father Joseph: https://maryknollmissionarchives.
org/?deceased-fathers-bro=father-joseph-a-hunt-mm

Maryknoll: Maryknoll Story in Little Tokyo: http://media.
discovernikkei.org/album/items/1/0/1058/maryknoll-dn.pdf

Swift, Father John: https://maryknollmissionarchives.org/?deceased-fathers-bro=father-john-f-swift-mm

HERO
KAZUO MASUDA

http://historicwintersburg.blogspot.com/2012/06/

http://cgm.smithsonianapa.org/stories/kazuo-masuda.html

https://encyclopedia.densho.org/Kazuo_Masuda/

INTERMENT/IMPRISONMENT

https://densho.org/

https://www.history.com/topics/world-war-ii/japanese-american-relocation

http://www.ushistory.org/us/51e.asp

https://www.smithsonianmag.com/history/injustice-japanese-
    americans-internment-camps-resonates-strongly-180961422/
https://www.archives.gov/education/lessons/japanese-relocation
https://www.pbs.org/childofcamp/index.html
https://www.realchangenews.org/2017/07/12/densho-project-
    uses-japanese-internment-start-conversation

LOYALTY OATH
http://www.rafu.com/2017/12/my-e-o-9066-story-former-inmates-
    of-tule-lake/
http://oberlinlibstaff.com/omeka_hist244/exhibits/show/
    japanese-internment/questions-of-loyalty
https://encyclopedia.densho.org/Loyalty_questionnaire/

PROTESTORS
Endo, Mitsuye: http://encyclopedia.densho.org/Mitsuye_Endo/
Hirabayashi, Gordon: http://encyclopedia.densho.org/Gordon_
    Hirabayashi/
Korematsu, Fred: https://advancingjustice-la.org/sites/default/
    files/UCRS%209_Fred_Korematsu_story%20r2.pdf
    https://densho.org/fred-korematsu-story-young-readers/

OTHER PROTESTORS
https://densho.org/beyond-the-big-four/
Yasui, Minoru: http://encyclopedia.densho.org/Minoru_Yasui/

WAR RELOCATION AUTHORITY
https://www.history.com/this-day-in-history/war-relocation-
    authority-is-established-in-united-states
https://www.politico.com/story/2018/03/18/fdr-sets-up-war-
    relocation-authority-march-18-1942-465793
https://drc.ohiolink.edu/handle/2374.GODORT/2

Made in the USA
Las Vegas, NV
26 April 2021